Introduction

Hulme Writer book *"A Great Big Dollop Of Hope"* (title courtesy of the great Hazel Bedford and proofread by Dame Sally Casey).

We would firstly like to thank those who have financially supported us. Without their kind support this book would have not been possible. Grateful thanks to the University of Manchester, Manchester City Council and Greater Manchester Mental Health Well Being Fund. The group would also like to thank all those who have worked in partnership with us, The On Top Of The World Hulme Project, and those that encouraged us From One Manchester, Lesley Bereton, Phil Lukes and Anna Bishop. We would also like to thank Hannah Berry who worked brilliantly with Esperance and her story.

The writing has been collated through the Hulme Writers group and contributions from Hulme residents. We met weekly at the beating heart of Hulme, the Aquarius centre before Covid 19 and after, we managed through Facebook, WhatsApp groups and as weather and rules permitted, outside classes.

The writing is testimony to the strength talent and determination of Hulme residents to not only survive, but to thrive in what has been a most difficult time. Never has it been so important to share our stories and support each other.

Our aim is to honour the voices of Hulme, to remember our stories of a community that has and are still going through, rapid development and gentrification.

We wanted to ensure that we not only left a legacy, and that we demonstrated that we are still here and integral to a changing Hulme where we bring our own skills talents and narratives.

This book contains stories, poetry, reminiscence, vignettes, blogs, speeches, memoirs, texts and WhatsApp messages by a group of *extremely talented* people. We have laughed cried and shared. And in doing so created friendship and bonds that sustain us, but above all gives us hope for our future in Hulme

Tina Cribbin
Creative Facilitator 2020

Hulme Writers

Is a group that works in partnership with *On Top of The World Hulme*. We are open to *all*; we welcome oral and written storytellers of *any* ability and experience. We hold weekly meetings where it is always a pleasure to see new faces. To have a cup of tea, some banter then we enjoy the silence as we write away our worries. To find out more please contact: Tinacribbin@gmail.com

Tina Cribbin

I am Tina a creative facilitator of Hulme Writers Group. I was raised in the concrete walkways of Hulme. I am immensely proud of my community and this book is just one example why! Surviving life, the Hulme way, fighting for justice with a smile.

Maize Reid

I am Mazie born in Jamaica in a time of war. I came to Moss Side in 1962 and life was hard. I grew my family. On my last count I have 25 grandchildren and 35 great-grandchildren. I moved to Hulme in 1993, I've met some lovely people and I'm taking life easy.

Hazel Bedford

I am Hazel, I was born in Ardwick in 1948. I moved to Hulme in 1968 and I am still living in the same house now. I retired in 2008 and I am now "a lady of leisure".

Alison Forbes

I am Allison, in my previous lives I have been a dance teacher, a caretaker, and now I am the published writer of seven books and I'm still writing! I live in St Georges very happily, being bossed about by my two beautiful cats.

Lil Luckham

I am Lil, yesterday I was looking at a picture of my twenty-year-old self; married, children and so unhappy, today's picture at 63 would show me fulfilled and happy from my life experiences.

Anne Finnegan

I am Anne, a Mancunian through and through. Brought up in Hulme a good Catholic girl (not). I was a dance teacher and mum and I am now co-ordinator for *On Top of The World Hulme*. I have collected many children over the years, but my own two boys are my joy.

Sonia James

I am Sonia, a so-called 'war baby' brought up like thousands of other by my Gran. Thank you Gran. Somehow, my children have grown into successful responsible adults, Life is good mostly.

Sally Casey

I am Sally, a child of Dublin, who holds a British Empire Medal from the Queen for my lifelong work in the community of Hulme. I am a Mancunian adult, a mother of four, grandmother and great grandmother. The best days of my life were growing my family manna to my sad soul, healing and happy now older but, still fighting.

Jean Bayode

I am Jean I lived in Hulme for many years but recently moved. Hulme is forever in my heart like my children who I am enormously proud of. Writing means the world to me.

Emily Oldfield

Emily was born in Burnley raised in Rossendale and has been writing for several years in Hulme. She joined Hulme writers in 2019. She is a writer, poet and is passionate about telling alternative stories of place and celebrating local communities, culture and music. She maintains that the writing group is one of the key features that made her feel "at home" in Hulme.

Esperance Kaligirwa

I am Esperance from the Democratic Republic of Congo. I have six children; four boys, two girls, and nine grandchildren. God has blessed me and has given me an incredibly happy life now.

Joana Salles

I am Joana Salles I was born in France 23 years ago. I moved around a lot growing up, in Hulme I finally feel like I belong somewhere. I don't talk much I listen and write. Sometimes I drink, it helps with the writing. That is probably why it's not always good!

<u>Hulme resident contributors</u>

John Sullivan, Frank Carlin, Frank Agar, Roy Bennett, Abigail Finch, Julie Sawdyk.

Contents

A Circle of Souls by Anne Finnegan

I saw a table of souls that kind of made a circle. They all shared a soul sewn together by time, hardship, love and grit. Memories shared, some forgotten, but all lived through.

A bottle of whiskey, tea, water, and wine staggered on the table oiling the songs and low mutterings of encouragement "Go on their Sally" "Jaysus now Frank"

Reliving the laws of the Hooleys, all must take a turn in entertaining the circle.

Celtic chains are re-linked and made strong by the melodic heartbeat earned from many a mile, and enclosed in the circle with no edges

Easter Sunday by Hazel Bedford

It is Easter Sunday morning I'm sat in my garden with a cup of tea. I am listening to the beautiful bird song, the buzzing of the bees and a squirrel running around a tree.

All appears peaceful in the world, you would not know from this that we have a World Pandemic with the Covid 19 Virus.

At times in my home the silence is deafening. For me and I'm sure for others it's a time of reflection, how I take things for granted. No matter what happens the World is still turning.

I have been messaging Loved ones, Family, Friends and my extended Aquarius Family. My phone as I'm sure yours also has been pinging with messages.

We are all in this together and this isolation we are in seems a little easier to bear knowing that love surround us as we are constantly made aware by the wonderful work that all the Front Line services are doing to help protect us.

I feel very blessed this Easter Sunday. Love to all

Covid by Joana Salles

The Covids are a family of 19. No one has ever heard of them; they've always been a quiet family living their life on the outskirt of the city. But the youngest could not bare the isolation from the real world anymore. Lying on her bed at night, in the room she shared with five of her siblings, she dreamt of exploring the world and meeting millions of people. One day, she decided to run away and follow her dreams. The first couple of days were magical. Everyone welcomed her in their home, brought her to local pubs and restaurants. She managed to see so much in so little time. But after a while everywhere she went, chaos followed. Maybe her parents were right, she wasn't ready for the outside world. Or maybe the outside world wasn't ready for her.

After a couple of weeks discovering China, people were avoiding her, giving her strange looks in the street. When walking in cities, grandmas and their grandchildren would run to the opposite sidewalk. It seemed like everyone was trying to keep at least a two-metre distance from her. So, naively, she thought it was time for a change. She followed a European family to the airport, hopped in a businessman's briefcase and on she went. They stopped in Iran first, but soon after her arrival, people's reaction copied the ones from China. She decided Europe might be her best chance to live the life she had always dreamt about in her small country house. After a couple of weeks of travelling around, joining in family reunions, business conferences and friends meet-ups she reached Italy. Despite some disappointing encounter, she started to feel more alive than ever. As soon as she arrived anywhere, people closed their doors on her. They wouldn't leave their houses for days but as soon as they let their guards down, she knew how to take advantage of them. She colonised their throats, their every thought. At the end of her journey, she realised she had made her dream come true. She travelled the world, met millions of people, but more importantly she had left a piece of herself in every place she visited. She impacted individuals, families, cities and her existence meant the world would never be the same, at least on some level.

Manctopia by Tina Cribbin

(This was written as a blog, in response to the programme Manctopia. A BBC programme which discussed the rapid housing development in central Manchester.)

Greetings from Hulme - apparently we are part of the "Donut of Deprivation" in Manchester as described by Tim Heatley. Yes, the hand in glove mate of the Lord Mayors of Manchester and Salford and the sellers of souls - Manchester City Council.

First let me start by saying the so called "donut of deprivation" is caused by greedy developers who have taken every available piece of land, community space, church, pub, and school. Our areas were not deprived until structural inequality became rampant through austerity and the selling of purposely driven down land and building were for sale in a move to destabilise the communities. In order to build unaffordable tower blocks for "city dwellers, who like to live differently" i.e. living 35 floors up looking down. Note that, looking "down" on us.

As someone who in Manctopia has been described as "disadvantaged, poor, deprived", I take great offence, I am more than your labels. By not showing communities actively engaged in fighting against the gentrification like most communities are, it left the viewer to assume that we are all just sitting passively as our lives disappear. We Are Not!

The fundamental message was about a capitalist understanding of housing where gold may drip from the shiny new tower blocks and trickle into our begging bowls and empty pockets but only if you are under 30 because through the lens of *Manctopia* no old people can live or visit the city centre. The monstrous developments are solely for investors to rent to young people. Anything outside of that population does not seem to exist in that world.

It does not show a community worn out with constant development and the cost of that on people's mental, emotional and physical health as you see your community being redeveloped year in and year out but not for the likes of you.

It does not show the fight at the coal face every day, when you must force yourself to the letterbox filled with dread with yet another development or absolute meaningless consultation. It does not show the anxiety and fear of people in the communities who have to fight for their basic human right of having a stable home. Our communities have become the city centre's dirty little secret.

I cannot express my absolute disgust that this was considered an intelligent documentary. The producers missed an opportunity to discuss important questions;

the irony of greedy developers working hand in hand with councils whilst smirking that he doesn't have to provide "affordable" housing and somehow air time is given to the greatest ego that ever walked. Walked on water as he really believed he was God and the absolute rubbish that he was helping the poor. Dry your eyes mate you're shameful.

Mazie Moon by Maize Reid and Tina Cribbin

She's only 8yrs old
But 4 am she rises every day

She's got the Bible to read
Miss Sara to feed.
She's to go to the river
To fill four kerosene containers with water.
No one could ever ask for a better daughter.

She begins her long walk to school
Hot with sweat and tiredness

And there is that lady on the side of the road
She must address
'Good morning Miss Mama!'
Has to get to school to be her very best

It's 4am
She's got the Bible to read
Miss Sara to feed
Has to fetch the water
Be a good daughter.
Run to school
'Good morning Miss Mama!'

Over and over
Over and over

A Great Big Dollop of Hope

Little Maisie Moon
Was forced to grow too soon

She walked with longer legs
Her burdens heavier
But never the less
'Good morning Miss Mama!'
Always respectable,
Always tried her best.
The lady nods and watches

A thousand good mornings later
When little Maisie Moon began to bloom.
Heavy heart, worn out feet
She looked up and began to greet
And Miss Mama say
'Don't call me Miss Mama!
I am your mother'

Confused and broken
She asked Miss Sara could this true?
'Am I not your child?
Did I never belong to you?'

She replied 'you were born in the sugar cane place
And I tried to raise you the best I can'
Tears roll down little Maisie Moon's face.
Was this her fate?
Her life plan?

The pain and burdens built her strong
She knew from young, that life was hard
But you just had to get on.

Now a great grandmother
Beautiful Maisie Moon

Sits with me and she tells me
I've his shirts wash
His food to cook
His medicine to bring
No time to sing

But Maisie's voice is beginning to grow
Out of a troubled past
Where she always put herself last

A new Maisie Moon arrives
The caged bird is beginning
To set herself free.

She writes from her heart
Maisie stands strong.
This is my story
I am here!
And I belong!

Things my Mam told me... by Lil Luckham

Mam constantly told me I was cheeky and gobby, but if she had only accepted I had a mind and opinions of my own, and I was fighting against being 'just a girl', Mam never failed to tell me there was something wrong with me because I hated dolls and prams and just wanted to get dirty and play football, if only she had said, "go on our Lil, score the winning goal for Manchester City with that great left foot of yours"

My periods started when I was 14 and my Mam told me to "stay away from dogs" as they would start humping my legs, oh I ran from so many dogs, and "don't kiss a boy as you will get pregnant", oh the kisses I missed out on. If only she had told me it was a natural transition into womanhood which would bring pain, mood swings, hygiene issues and children, but poor Mam, you were so embarrassed weren't you, I am sorry.

Mam brought me up to believe sex was dirty and most men were beasts, oh Mam Dad never stood a chance. I feel sad for both, that my Mam never experienced the joy and intimacy of sex and my emotional, loving Dad was shut out.

As older adults we laughed with her and teased her, I asked her if she had ever had an orgasm, the full bottle of Holy water she always had beside her was tipped over my head. Mam I would have loved you to have said to me, if only once, "I did enjoy it".

My Mam told me never say sorry unless you really mean it, only forgive when you have really forgiven and just be nice to people and they will be nice to you. Thank you, Mary G, I wouldn't change a word of THAT advice.

Our man Frank by Christopher Finnegan

He lives in the run-down high rise flat
20 deck a day is what his pension pays
Perhaps a pack of biscuits but that's about it
And in his armchair, that's where he'll sit

A sweeter man you never did see
With a voice like thunder and the arms of a tree
Big old fella, sure he carried the hod
But now he's grown older, limbs can't take the plod

"Do it when you're young" he tells me every Wednesday
A joke and a warning said in his own special way
Like chatting to your Grandad on the day you go round
But with a sadness in his tone a dull thudding sound

He's a natural-born, scorned and torn Irish storyteller

His mind is a pub, a cup, a pint and a whiskey and a
shelter
Look into his eyes you'll see the path of a true *Seanchai*
The places in which bore and stores his stories and his
memories

Fairy circles, funeral marching mice, card games with
the devil, and the red eyed dog
Ancient talking turtles, the willow'o'the wisp, the
banshees scream in the midnight fog

An art of communication from a bygone era
When people sat closer and heard thing clearer
Where the pub was the hub, your word meant the world
Having *craic* till the *craic* healings cracks telling pearls

The laughing, the crying, the kissing, the lying, the
births and the debts the dying and the bets
The lounge and the vault where the women would halt,
fighting fists, getting pissed, rebel song persists
The scraps and the tabs, the ladies, the loss, pool tables,
racial labels the guilt of getting off
Through it all the man stood tall, but he feels there's
something he missed cos no now when he looks
around he's sorely found that it's no longer existing

Nowadays He sits in his chair and smokes away
All day and all night but hey, what can he say?
The shops too far and no-one's coming over
"I'll just go tomorrow if I can shift these boulders"

He Lives on the 2nd floor and he can't take the stairs
So, if the lift is broken, he's not going anywhere
The Students on the bottom floor living it up
Unaware and uncaring of the man up above

A Great Big Dollop of Hope

So, forgive me for saying this but how can it be
That this is what it took for people to see
And even still people move with eyes closed
Bumping into realities of living home alone

It's funny how the world turns round now innit?
Last week you were fine but now you're Frantic and you're spinning
Locked in-doors with nowhere to go
Well that's how Frank's felt for 20 years or more

Isolation is a beast it's a leech if you let it
But what if those you know don't see it or get it
There's no one to lean on so you just let it feast
Living with a demon but you can't call on the priest

Rona is bold, she'll take every corner
But Frank won't be told he's an old-fashioned soldier
He's built for this Demic let it brush of his shoulder
Take a leaf from his book in his image we should mould

Living life in a high rise, he's sees the world from on top
He's on top of the world but he's too far from shops
Too far from the sound, the ground and the people
Yes he needs to touch down but the fall might be Lethal

So now you're by yourself or you're stuck inside with friends
Some say life is short don't let it drive you round the bend
But some can make it way too long you feel like you're condemned
But it won't take long, don't you worry, soon you'll be back on the mend

But when this is over and you go back to your job

Go back to your office and pick back up your lot
Remember that Frank is still all alone
Watching the world on high from his lonely throne

A king in his space with a mind gone to waste
He'll smoke and he'll drink, whilst he waits there for fate
But don't fret just yet because Frank's not truly alone
There's thousands just like him, sat alone their homes

A knock at the door or a call on the phone
Arms wrapping around just to make them feel whole
Touch hunger's real for the body and the soul
These communities of ghosts hidden behind concrete and stone

We give thanks by Tina Cribbin

And the tears and fears
I'm facing don't only belong to me.
It's another dark marker in this world's history

All the children, mothers, fathers, aunts, uncles
Brothers and sisters all survive the best we can
Even though we miss ya

In spaced out queues
We are Mancs
We have a laugh
Sing the blues
Two by two
But only one allowed to shop

We are forced to wear protective masks.
Rubber gloves as well
Sanitised and insecticide
Make for an unbearable hell

But we are Mancs
We give thanks
To the nurses
The carers
The unseen heroes
Who play their roles
Silently

The weak and the old
Stoic and alone
Can teach us a thing or two

With love laughter and light.
Us Mancs know how to fight
We soldier on heroically
Covid 19 can never stop
The poetry
The enormity of our strength

Love will break the fences
And when the world recommences

We
Hug
Hold hands
Chat
Breathe in air without a filter mask
At last
At last
At last!

Another day by Sonia James

And another day comes to an end in our new reality.
Have I turned into Alice? I don't remember falling down
a rabbit hole. Such strange times and happenings. Every

country believing they are right in how they deal with this new reality. To lock down or not. Mask wearing compulsory or voluntary or not to care at all. So much confusion and anger. Authoritarian leaders using this time to beat their citizens to the ground, quite literally in some cases. To continue to rape their countries for their own personal greed and care nought for doing so. In this almost apocalyptic time we are truly blessed if we have friends to turn to, that our loved ones are safe and believe that as soon as we can, we are able to stand at the graves, weep and tear our hair for those we lost and were not allowed to hold at the end. Our churches are closed so where to turn for solace for those that believe. To our friends and families, hold them close in our hearts and don't let go. Thank your Gods for the strength you find and share it. Share the love cos that's all we have right now.

I see the numbers of the poor deceased. They're frightening

No time for peace

I cannot even begin to imagine the grief of the thousands upon thousands of poor families.

Tears shed span the world's circumference

Linked by sadness holds no comfort.

In this new existence we make a new inventory.

To cherish our loved ones and cherish each special moment imprint them upon our memory

And learn to live in the moment stop chasing material dreams. What we've learned from this love is what will get us through this.

In the face of adversity, the human race shows its face with grace, love, and empathy. Let us not forget that after this tragedy.

We Felt Free to Delete by Sonia James

We've been killing our planet for years
Now here we are in this veil of tears
I want to scoop up all those I love
Is this why astronauts keep looking above
There are plenty of planets up there
Just need to find one with water and air
But I have to ask does mankind deserve it?
It's our own fault we're knee deep in shit
Most of mankind is gregarious,
 We huddle together in tribes
Now we see what we've done we are furious
But take no personal blame, righteous vibes.
If we survive this terrifying time
Will I care about you and yours?
No. Only mine.

Artichoke Dip by Tina Cribbin

We come in unveiled
In our poverty
With our pot to piss in.

At the food bank we all say it's crap,
it is a disgrace
But still we are here just in case.
No, not because we need it.
We will not give them that!

Happy Shopper 19p mushy peas,
Next to tins of fish chowder,
Packets of fennel dust
Alongside smart price biscuits
And sanitary towels.

The jars of artichokes and salmon mousse
Look down their noses at me
All middle-class swagger, and shiny entitlement,
You have no idea how to cook me

I smile as they land in my basket,
Shocked and shitting it.
Worried about being cooked in B and M pans
Instead of being steamed and pampered
In pro cooks finest.

That's what's happens artichokes in our world.
You just must make do
And fit.
When your life goes off script.

Fk it I say
The dog will eat well tonight

Things that make me glad to be alive by Hazel Bedford

5 Places I'd like to visit. 5 People that make me happy.

Glad	Visit	People
Sunny skies	Madeira	Bob Ross
Birds song	Paris	My Family
Friends	Rome	Louise.
The Seasons	Llandudno	Pep Guardiola.
Music	Edinburgh	Friends.

I'm off on an Adventure by Hazel Bedford

I'll first go to Madeira, a place I have always wanted to go, with its rugged Coast Line. I arrived in the morning and once I had left my luggage in my room, which by the way was amazing, I went for a walk around the town. On this walk I took in some of the wonderful views out to sea, whilst on this walk I bumped into Bob Ross the American Painter (not literally), Bob had gone to Madeira for some inspiration for a painting he could do which would be different from his normal landscapes. We had a good conversation, he instructed me on how I could achieve his art work.

My next stop was Paris – a place I love, to me it's magical, it was just after Christmas, early January, the Champs Elysée still had its Blue Lights all the way down to the Arc de Triomphe. I went there with my Goddaughter Louise. It was just a GIRLS (ha ha) weekend. Couldn't help doing some shopping, Perfume, Eye Shadow and of course a trip to Fauchon for some Chocolates. We also took a trip on the Open Top Bus to see all the sights and also took a boat ride on the Seine and of course we went up the Eiffel Tower, After this trip Louise returned home and I carried on with my adventure.

My next stop was Rome, I wanted to go and see the Vatican and Vatican City, also I wanted to see the Trevi Fountain and throw a coin in. Taking a well-earned break at a cafe, I decided I would sit outside to drink my Coffee and a Ammareto. I could not believe my eyes when I noticed sitting outside as well, only Pep Guardiola, along with his family, they had taken a trip from his home in Spain to do some sight seeing. When

I left the cafe, they were all still there.

My next stop would be in the UK - Llandudno with its beautiful Promanade and Pier. You can walk for ages, even walk up the Great Orme if you like to exert yourself more. Along with my family we decided to do this but not everyone wanted to walk that far so some took the Tram and we all met at the top and had a great time.

My fifth and final stop is Edinburgh. I have gone on this trip with my friends, we took a coach trip 5 days - 4 nights. We stayed in a beautiful hotel, we had a wonderful time at the Edinburgh Tattoo, we also took a tour of the Castle and couldn't resist the Royal Mile and the Royal Botanic Gardens, we also had time to explore the city ourselves. During these imaginary adventures, a good time was had by all. - of that I am sure.

The Same Conversation by Tina Cribbin

I walk each day around my tower block 30 times with a few breathers. I'm not built for speed. Since the lockdown I treasure every moment I can get outside. Each morning on my rounds my old fella comes to meet me. He is past 80 walks with a stoop now, but with the happiest eyes you would ever see. He goes for his daily walk but before that we have the same conversation every day.

Him: Hiya how's yourself then, it's a bit breezy/fresh/lovely.

Me: it is, how's you?.

Him: this virus thing is getting worse (he means he's afraid)

Me: I know it's just a case of waiting (I mean I'm afraid too)

Him: I've had my life I'm concerned for the young ones not going to work (Him I am accepting that I am close to the age people die.)

Me: What do you mean, you've had your life, you're going nowhere

We both laugh

(I mean I can't imagine living in the flats with you not around, you light up the place. I will not accept that.

Him: it is the grandkids I'm missing, sure even in the war you saw your family and the pubs were open! (He means he's lonely, and remembering all his friends who are not here. He is on limited time and wants to spend it with family)

Me: I know, after this walk I am in all day looking at four walls. Sending me stir crazy (I mean I know how you feel I feel lonely too. You're not alone)

Him: Ah sure what can we do we've just got to make the best of it (Him, despite how I feel I don't give up)

Me: Yes, we just put one foot in front on the other. (I mean despite how I feel, I won't give up either)

Him, well that's it girl you're right (He means we both have a job to do)

We both walk off smiling knowing we are both frightened, but both cared about. The same conversation that does not mention his love fills me every day and helps me to just keep putting one foot in front of the other. I keep my face to the sun.

The Holiday by Jean Boyode

There was a holiday on offer "look Sophie, Turkey 8th of June for two weeks. It's £400 all inclusive, let's go in and have a look at it."

"Hi, can I book this holiday advertised in the shop

window"

"Yes" said the tourist operator, "How many is it for?"

"It's for two adults, myself Alan Baxter, and my wife Sophie Baxter."

"Ok I will ring through now and make the booking. Here is all the information for departure. You have a double room with tea and coffee making facilities. With en suite shower room and balcony sea facing. You are on the 2nd floor and your room number is 295. When you arrive, you will be given a welcome pack keys and voucher for your stay."

"Well that is all booked" said Sophie "shall we treat ourselves to a nice lunch as well? I fancy a nice steak." We have been here before I remember it. Come on let's go and grab a table. Alan asked the waitress for a menu. Sophie placed her order of well-done steak with chips and salad. Alan wanted the same but his steak to be medium rare. The waitress asked would you like wine? "Yes" of course replied Alan we would prefer red. "Ok" said the waitress thank you for your order.

Alan said I've got a surprise for your birthday. Sophie could see Alan's legs twitching, his hands were shaking and sweaty. "Give me your index finger and then he opened the box and it was a gold ring with sparkling diamonds like the stars. Alan placed it on her finger and whispered, "this is for my paradise Happy Birthday darling in advance and many more to come". "Oh, thank you said Sophie I'm so grateful it's a wonderful gift." Alan said to the waitress can we have one millionaire's dessert and one toffee ice cream. It was brought out a short time later a silver tray. Both were incredibly happy.

On the day of departure Sophie wanted to look at the shops at the airport to get some cheap cigs and brandy. After they checked in their luggage they went to the bar and ordered a brandy and coke for Sophie and a pint for himself. He gave the waitress a tip of two pounds and she was delighted. I fancy something light. Let's get a fresh sandwich said Sophie. "Come on now" said Alan "it is time to board our plane to Turkey. I will let you sit near the window" said Alan. Both put their seatbelts on and slept through the flight. Sophie nudged Alan look darling we have landed, they made their way to the hotel and checked in and were given a welcome pack with the times for breakfast, lunch and dinner. They were so tired they just slept in the hotel room until the next day. Morning said Alan "let's go and have breakfast then afterwards we shall go to the beach and get to know the locals."

After strolling along the beautiful beach one of the locals said, "Hi my name is Salim, come into my restaurant I am pleased to meet you. What are your names." Sophie said, "my name is Sophie, and this is my husband Alan". Alan ordered two coffees; Salim brought the coffees. and he also brought his card as he said he owns different music and entertainment venues including cruises. How much is the cruise said Sophie? If you book it through me its five included is the mud bath and outdoor jacuzzi "Okay said Alan, we will book it.

Alan asked if they could do the boat trip today. Salim said yes it leaves at noon from the beach. Then his friend came in and said his name was bloody gorgeous. He walked in and said Hello what is your name? My name is Sophie, and this is Alan. "They call me bloody gorgeous because I like the chicks". And we all began to laugh. Yes, you have to have a sense of humour working in the sun all day.

They returned at noon for the cruise the boat started to move the music was blaring it was a beautiful sunny as they cruised around the smaller islands. "Look Alan! Turtles in the water I can see them so clear." Come on said Alan they are serving lunch. The waiters served delicious fish and salad while the young boys were jumping into the sea. The music was loud, and Alan said "let's dance" Bob Marley was on loudspeaker and everyone was enjoying themselves. After the sun began to set, they returned and had an evening stroll along the beach. Afterwards they had a nice coffee with Salim. Salim asked if they enjoyed the trip. "Oh, it was amazing" said Sophie. "It's honestly been the best day of my life."

Do not forget the pensioners by Sally Casey

As Angela Merkel said today, "Germany must not forget the pensioners, they rebuilt the country after the war."

Well I am bitter in that we will be the last on the list to be allowed to roam free when the lockdown is lifted. They are more worried about children not being looked after. Well let their parents take responsibility for them, those on the front line are in a different category altogether, it's wonderful that WhatsApp has brought so many of us together.

We are there for each other come hell or high water.

If I wash another cup or take another six spoons out of the water, I'll fling them into the garden!

Who are the six people using them, I'm the only one who drinks tea, so whoever you are, come out and identify yourself?

Beating the Blues by Hazel Bedford

I am hearing words I have never heard before from political parties throughout the UK.

I try to remember them – but alas I can't – maybe their words just wash over me.

I don't bother to listen every day because it only brings me down.

I am trying extremely hard to keep upbeat, now each day I am succeeding.

I know I have a wealth of friends that are with me on this strange journey.

We will all falter at one time or another, but there are friends who will encourage us to put one foot in front of the other on this journey.

Lockdown Teachings by Abigail Finch

If being on lockdown has taught me one thing,

It is to grasp the moment and enjoy this wonderful world we live in.

Never again will I cancel plans with my friends,

I am dreaming of the long summer evenings together when this all ends.

Leaving things for a 'special occasion' is a thing of the past,

BEING ALIVE is the special occasion and I hope this mindset lasts.

My family are my everything, it has taken this for me to see,

I need to make time for the ones I love – just as they make time for me.

I will stop over-thinking things and take chances every day,

No more worrying about everything, I will start living for today.
When this is all over, we will not take our health for granted again,
'Health is wealth' is the new mantra and our attitude towards life will never be the same.

Fatopia by Tina Cribbin

Indignity of obesity
And fat shaming ingenuity
Trying to redefine the shape of women's beauty
I have to lose weight,
Of this thing,
In order to fit,
I need to despise its curves
Its voluptuous allure.
Its softness, its lumps and bumps of life stories,
Its ageing signs of being over forty.

I must be stick thin in order to be visible,
Highlighted hair and botoxed face
Just in case I show signs of being miserable.
My bras designed for balconies
To minimise to emphasise
To hide the surprise of real breasts when they are let loose.

Let your inner big girl out!
Let her scream and shout.
Just say no to the starving media atrocities,
That kills our girls,
Defines our world view of understanding beauty.
I am screaming at society,
Sick of it screening my shape,

Causing me to hate,
Allowing my body shape to define the whole of me.

You're killing the soul of me!
But, me
I'm coming right fat at yer!
I'm walking with a bounce,
Not giving you an ounce.
I am here to propagate
That fatness wins over hate.
That brains, beauty and age coexist,
That real women don't need your fix.
I'm an ageing natural beauty very happy with my bootie

Barry White by Tina Cribbin

On lockdown this woman did not care.
I admire her spirit her humour
It takes you unawares.

I'm going to win at bingo
I need that wireless too.
I have got a boyfriend he's only 22

I want Barry White
I can just imagine him turning up at my door
But he's dead.

We laughed and laughed and shook our heads.
This little firecracker is a vision to behold.
A woman of strength who will not be told

She won the bingo she got the full house!
We all clapped and cheered
But she was still giving out

She turned on the wireless and gave me that stare

What is this crap? Barry White is not in there!

So, bless you darling, for simply being you.
In lockdown days sometimes, it's hard to get through.

Your priorities and enthusiasm for life put me to shame.
I'm so glad you made it to our bingo game

I would like my life by Jean Bayode

I would like my life to be good so that I can be comfortable with my family and spend quality time with them. I would like to be able to provide all the things that they need. I want to see my family growing up nicely and enjoy having fun with them and go out for meals and holidays. I would like to be able to buy them nice presents for birthday and Christmas. I also want us to have nice family parties together

Tower Block Blues by Tina Cribbin

(This is another blog that I was asked to write in response to Covid 19)

My tower block tastes of fear and panic. It is in the screech of metal as the security gates open. It is in the squeaky one plastic hand sanitizer that is stiff, due to the lack of use. It is the smell of extra strong disinfectant that is mixed with fear and lost routines as we try to navigate getting to our floor level without touching anything. It looks daunting. My sister calls it a metal prison. But I call it home.

I should be used to fear after Grenfell, and the two years of upheaval cladding removal, new heat and fire sensors. I should be used to living a life I have little control over, but I am not.

This pandemic has brought living differently to a

whole new level. You have all the time in the world to worry if one person gets it in the block. Will we all get it? We have no choice but to use the communal space. Frightened eyes scurrying away from each other in corridors held in breath as we run into our personal boxes.

The daily living of looking out the window to see the roads below. The world becoming emptier, and emptier, and the view across the road yet another tower block with same sense of despair we can only look at each other. And then the panic inside you grows and grows but you have nowhere to take it. The doctors is closed and you are too frightened to go outside because the texts from the NHS put the fear of god in you. I see carers who cannot get into the block because they haven't got the security codes, I see food parcels being dropped off in see through bags. The indignity of the disregarded because we dared to get old.

So, you sit with your fear and the loneliness in a little small box in the sky. Feeling anonymous and forgotten. I am jealous of people in lockdown sharing posts about their gardens, we have a small balcony where its shoulder level no sitting out on the balcony with a glass of wine for us. I am sure they thought it would protect against accidents and suicides. Well it did not stop the latter. It only increased your sense of otherness of not being enough to warrant a bit of sunshine of your face.

And then I dared to take a risk…

Because you can die of this virus, but you can also die inside, and I was tired of seeing my neighbours lonely but resigned faces. Injustice etched into the lines on our faces. There are many ways to die here.

Before the pandemic, my life was community. It was

my medicine for the bipolar disorder I have been labelled with. And it worked, I functioned and contributed, and I was happy because supporting others got me through any dark days. We have a project called *Top Of The World Hulme*. It is run by me, Anne and Christopher Finnegan, where we promote social support and advocacy among older tower block tenants through arts and creativity. We run a social drop in but also drama and creative writing groups, a *Seanchai* café (Irish storyteller), Hooleys (Party) nights, and a savings club. We are part of a network called GM Savers which is all about looking after each other, making plans together for your community, and networking groups together across the city to share ideas.

Since lockdown we have been monitoring needs among all our members and signposting them for food parcels and other support. We started a daily ring round. I can still hear the sobs from an older lady who apologised to me because she could not stop crying, or the woman whose voice had gone because she had not talked to anyone in so long. Or my neighbour Joe who said at least in the war you got to see your family and the pubs were open! Most talked of the absolute isolation and fear. And that somehow because of the media narrative they were at fault because of their age. It was clear what was needed was more than the practicalities for those isolating. We needed joy and hope and a sense of not being alone.

We started *Get Busy On Your Balcony!* We brought the music, enthusiasm and love. It was such a sense of freedom as we sang up to the block "I just called to say I love you" by Stevie Wonder. As we saw smiling faces coming on to their balconies.

Since then we have regular balcony bingo sessions

and have social distanced disco dancing. Our next plan is street theatre.

Living under lockdown is hard, this does not solve all the problems, but it recognises that tower block dwellers are human with spirits and soul that also need nourishing. As I step into my lift and it rises so does the hope that somehow, we can make it through.

Stupid We Are Not! by Sonia James

We may only be the masses, but stupid we are not.
Give us a yard, we won't hang ourselves, that's not in our plot.
"They" think they hold all the power, the money and the means,
We can see through their ruse; this new rule is not what it seems.

Someone who thinks he's important, because he has power over you, over me,
We're not allowed to criticise, well we did, and now see.
"They" say they are loosening the lockdown, thinking we will forget!
Five years to us is nothing, we will survive and get our own back yet.

All the World's a Stage by Hazel Bedford

Shakespeare once said, "All the world's a stage and the people are merely players." How true is this at the present time, you only need to look and listen today to know that there are players and then there are Actors.

The world's stage now is turbulent. My theory for this is that the Politicians are not players they are actors who appear to be on our side, but their actions don't seem to correspond. In some countries of the world they have Waves of unrest which seems to be spreading.

The Players, (you and I) are worn out trying to understand what the bulletins mean, it is exceedingly difficult to know what we are, or what we are not supposed to be doing. I do not know what the answer is but maybe, just maybe, if the Politicians became players instead of actors we would be on a level playing Field.

Dreading what today's bulletin from the Actors will be.

A circle of Souls by Jean Bayode

Jimmy, Kieran, Beverley and Kathleen were all stood in a circle wearing new shoes. Jimmy had shiny lace ups. "Jimmy why are you showing off your shoes? Is it because they are new?" Kathleen said they need a polish Jimmy you need to see your face in them.

Place by Sally Casey

I have been put in my place since early March 2020. Not a place I wanted to be guided to as The Place where I will spend my days and nights until I'm told! Right, you can now leave your space once a day for one hour.

Why Me.? Did they pick on me because I will not make a fuss. Well, who would I make a fuss to?
They would have made condescending remarks to me and told me that it was for the good of my health.

Which section of my health. Do they know that (it) did not know where I live? There were no 111 calls made from my phone, no need for an ambulance to speed its way to test me for (it). (It) did not find my Place.

But who do I contact for earache, mouth ulcers, bad tummy, sore knees, creaking neck, weird spots on my forehead that decided that it was the perfect place to take up residence, rent free? What were they, why me, I never had them as a teenager, so why now? Did they know where my Place was? Who sent them?

They said, contact us if you need a doctor, do not sit in your place if you feel unwell. BUT, to visit these Places, you must be healthy.

Twelve weeks in this place has defined my life in a way that has me questioning, what now, where now, how now. My life is now determined by them who tell me that my place is to listen and be instructed by the knowledgeable ones who will tell me if I can leave my Place and when.

Will I end up in a Gulag where my life will be a set of traffic lights to adhere to. (It) may like this Place so much that it will stay for ever and ever. What then!

Maybe I Could? by Sonia James

Maybe I could learn to cook, but buy which ingredients? Where?
Maybe I could do allsorts, I have already cut my hair.
Maybe I could learn to knit, or maybe even sew.
But where to get the stuff for that, I am locked indoors, you know.
I could try the internet, that would teach me how.

But all that concentration gives me a sweaty brow.
I'm a hoarder with my many books and hate to lend them out.
Ok, so I'm rationing that pastime, don't be in any doubt.
So that's my life for now, this home is a news free zone.
I'll read my books, watch some selective TV, I'll be ok at home.

It's Okay by Tina Cribbin

If I am afraid for a while
It's ok
The world feels out of focus,
My dreams have gone astray
It's ok to feel the things we feel; afraid lonely, sad, angry
we are entitled to them too
It's not possible to be upbeat all the time but I don't
think acknowledging your feelings leaves you weak or
less kind.
We will all have our wobbles, I had one yesterday the
poisoned parrot came out to have his say. All the demons
I had been chasing felt like they never went away
The panic monster woken.
I will have feed him tokens based on pacing
Forever tracing how awful my life is
And God that monster loves a catastrophe!
I befriend him most of the day. Survived it silently.
You know how it is.
But as night turned to light there was faintest crack.
A breath of calmness cooled my back.
In that moment it is all it took to know the storms
passing.
I rest then sneak a look.
Although fragile and cautious I will begin again
Start to think when this will all end.
And all people will come back, and the earth will breathe
easier for its rest.
We will learn to be gentler with the earth and fellow
man.
As sure as night follows day, I'm sure we can

Today is... by Hazel Bedford

Today is… I can't remember what the number is, of staying isolated from friends and family. Things and time are no longer clear. Days seem to morph into one another. I no longer keep to any sort of schedule. I have a long to do list, but at present it does not seem that important. Nothing comes easy except for the fact that I know I have the love and support of family, friends and finally, YOU LOT x

My pen is poised by Sonia James

Ok, so now my pen is poised to write,
I've been manic today, gave everyone a fright,
Because yesterday I behaved like I was a sloth,
'For goodness sake' said my son, you cannot be both
'Why not?' I asked him, 'I can be what I choose,
Some days you win and some days you lose'.
So now I'm wondering what will happen tomorrow,
Well whatever it is, if we're virus free, then no sorrow.

Getting Through by Joana Salles

Day 43 – I am a mess. I've hit rock bottom. The only way to go is up from now on. I doubt myself in everything I set myself to do. Maybe I just hate everyone because they're better than me, and they have the guts to be. They are not stuck on their bedroom floor all day and all night long complaining how hard and shit life is. And even when it is, they just pick themselves up and do something to make it more bearable. Life is a journey; it is okay to make a couple of stops on the way. Let your legs be free. But you cannot constantly wonder if you picked the right colour for your car. Or if the music you chose is the right soundtrack for your travels. Or whether you should have left that hitch-hiker on the side of the road. Yes, you will go over the speed limit sometimes, maybe even get a ticket for not wearing your seatbelt. If you don't go to court for a hit and run, you gotta keep going.

You don't have to follow the main road, or even a road at all. Create your own paths as you go, leave a mark as long as it's not on the environment. Throw out the toxic passengers that smoke, keep the ones that bring healthy snacks, and don't judge your music choice but sing along to anything just for the fun of it. Don't ban anything apart from mood killers. Be tolerant, loving, and kind. Get creative, loud and confident. Don't hate. Dance. Dance to the rhythm of life. Dance to your own rhythm and follow your own beat.

The Elixir of life by Sonia James

A lot of infectious giggling and some raucous laughter too
It's those young hippy type guys who make their very own brew
They can be heard all around, the stairs to our flats
You know the ones I mean, they wear those Fedora hats
They are very generous when it comes to party time
It's just where to hold it, his, hers, or mine?
The last party time I learned a lot I hadn't known
Oh yes, I can honestly say my knowledge of "stuff" has grown

Down the Road by Jean Bayode

Stacey and Macey went off walking down the road, first on the left. They get to forty-one and Stacey knocks.

"Hi Stacey, what are you doing here?"

"I've come to see you Uncle Barney"

"Come in then"

He opened the door wider to let them in. They went in and saw such a beautiful house. Uncle Barney said, "Do you two young ladies like a drink?"

"Yes please" said Stacey"

"What can I get you?" said Uncle Barney.

"Prosecco please!" they both replied.

When This is All Over by Sonia James

Don't be naive
We're humans, destructive and selfish indeed
About the hoarding of loo rolls, the greed for flour,
The masks and gloves some wore hour after hour
Receiving annoying texts and unwanted messages
Angry about the lack of vegetarian sausages.
About the people who think rules don't apply to them
And think all will be back to normal when
We see our earth starting to repair and then
We revert to our old way's selfishness and mayhem
You know the saying 'old habits die hard'
Well that's humans, but we'll pretend we were dealt this card
No I don't think this virus will change us like magic
I think we will revert to our old habits

Not So Much Pollution by Sonia James

Not so much pollution, look how very blue is the sky.
Are the birds singing louder, maybe, but I wonder why?
Is it the lack of noise that we humans always cause?
It's time to stop and listen, to look, to rest, to pause

So let's enjoy this period of enforced and lazy time
And open your heart, make a new friend, all will turn

out fine
Open your heart and your mind because all new things
are there
Grab each day with both hands, fear no news, just be
aware
Of all the wonderful things that are free
Of all the love and friendship, it's there, look and see

The Music Played by Sonia James

The music played louder than loud
They were all there, the family type crowd
Chatting to faces, of late rarely seen
Hello, how are ya, how have you been
Masks, visors, cover ups, gloves and all
It made no difference we all had a ball
A new skill was learned megaphone calling
Well much more ladylike than just outright bawling
We all danced without a partner that night
But it was such fun and it just seemed right
Keeping your distance was quickly learned
But we hope and pray it will be short termed
So the next time the lockdown is making us blue
We will shout, come on let's party and round up our
crew

Getting Ready for the Summer by Sonia James

I'm getting ready for the summer season
All my clothes are laid out on my bed
Don't worry, I've not lost my reason,
I know it's all in my head,
But I'm bored now and look it's coming
So I've washed all my summer tops

Normal times we'd be out there sunning
So let's brighten the gloom, wear a colour that pops
I've decided I'm going to start today
I'm wearing my favourite summer skirt
Even though I know there is nowhere to play,
It'll brighten my spirit and that can't hurt
All these weeks not seeing family or friends,
But we've lived through life's trials, we'll survive this, we're strong
Sometimes it's lonely and could send us round the bend.
I won't give up, I'll beat fiercely on my drum and sing louder, my life affirming song

All will be well by Sonia James

All will be well guys. We got this down to a fine art now. Whatever 'they' say, we do whatever keeps us sane. Our group is strong and when we have a wobble we know where to turn for support and it's our safety valve. Have a giggle, have a cry or whatever you need to get you through. Always someone here to lean on, I've found or to give a shoulder to if you're having a better day. Love you guys.

Enough by Sonia James

I want to scream and tear my hair; I want to rant and rave
This true-blue attitude, stiff upper lip, I'm sick of being brave
I'm not particularly worried I'll be brought down by this pandemic,
I don't understand a lot of the statistics I'm not an academic.
Now I'm told I can go out and wander wherever I

please,
But I must still wear my mask just in case I sneeze.
It's no longer enough for me and I've tried, I've really tried,
But maybe I'd feel better if I just cried and cried and cried?
But where would be the release in that it would just make my eyes all red
I still want to scream and shout, maybe I should have stayed in bed!

Moody Weather by Hazel Bedford

The weather reflects my mood today. Stayed in bed too long this morning. Just been doing some little jobs and then decided to sweep and weed outside the house, down the fence, felt like over the hills and far away. I have been blown and bashed by the wind and I look like a tramp. Roll on tomorrow hope we are not given any more confusing, rubbish, throw in the bin trash from "the powers that be" which should be titled "the wallies that haven't got a clue" Or I'm just I being unkind today. Love to all

When It's All Over by Hazel Bedford

Morning all, ladies, ladies what is all this about?

The first place I will visit is my favourite Chippy on Tib Street for a Pensioners Meal, Fish and Chips, Mushy Peas, Tea and Bread and Butter.

The first person I would like to see, would find it hard to choose one person, but it would have to be my Family and loved ones.

The first thing I would buy is a difficult one. I cannot say clothes because I have been buying online.

No, my minds gone blank – suggestions please.

Llandudno Walk by Sally Casey

I want to go on a train or in a car to Llandudno. I want to walk along the prom, seagulls or not chasing me for my 99, with a chocolate flake stuck down inside of it. I'll knock one of them out if he or his mates come near me.

I'm the one who's been in lockdown, not them. And then when I get tired, I am

Going for fish and chips, then I'm going to the shops to see what's in the 70pc off sale. They must be designer, after all by that time I'll be size 10. I just know it.!!!! Who's laughing. It is you Sonia.

I am then going for an exceptionally large Jameson& dry ginger with 2 pieces of ice. I may reorder if I so wish.

I may stay overnight, but in a hotel, no bed and breakfast for me, I need spoiling.

I have been in lockdown you know.

I may take a taxi home if I am so inclined.

I feel that I need to take care of myself, just in case there maybe someone near enough to me to infect me with their bad breath or other bodily odours if you get my drift, or theirs.

Well, I've booked my rail ticket and the grand hotel, all I need now is for Big Boris to release me from my ivory tower.

Bon Voyage

After by Anne Finnegan

I want to have an alfresco lunch on a warm sunny Mediterranean shore with nice wine and people I love. Lounge in easy chairs and luscious surroundings, while we listen to the sea and watch the boats, surfers and fishermen. Everyone relaxed and happy.

As the sun goes down, I will move onto dinner with twinkling lights inviting music and a soft breeze, we will eat some more, drink a lot more! Dance and laugh our hearts sadness away.

Just how I feel by Sonia James

Sorry guys. It's just how I feel today. I'm so sad. I miss my family. But I'm angry too. "How can I make them forget about Dominic Cummings travel log" thinks Boris. "Oh I know, let's ease lockdown so people can go out and buy a new car, there's no pollution now anyway so I've met the safety limits". Hah, who's a clever boy then? Well, not us that is for sure. The listeners, the helpers, the 'do as you're told, stay at home' majority. I've had a long hard cry. Better out than in. You'll have heard, Dance like no-one can see you, and, sing like no-one can hear you, well today is my cry day. As long, and as loud as I like. And forget the stiff upper lip

Sonia, my guiding star by Sally Casey

You are saying what we feel, I am so disgusted with that moron, and his lying get of an advisor. Let us all shout Boo Boris as we rattle our pans and pots on Thursday for our angels.

I feel degraded that I listened to his whining voice for so many weeks. He is the gutless slime-ball that I always thought he was.

Ministers have been quoted as saying what an idiot Dominic Cummins is. He would start a row for the sake of it.

So, we are still the meek and the mild, he has not killed us all off... YET. So, what next for us?

Sonia, you are missing your family and you are so entitled to be sad and upset. You have been my guiding star for ten weeks. When I was down you lifted me up, well now jump on my back and I will carry your sadness, and you, to somewhere nice, I'm only carrying you because you've got a sore knee.

I've got a bad back, so hopefully you've not put on too much weight in the last week. Here is a big hug from me to you. Love you to the moon and back. Bloody hell that's a long way, isn't it!

Headless Families by Sonia James

It was after the Falklands war and our force's husbands were sent to the island periodically on detachment. As an Air Traffic Controller, mine spent 3 months there, and loved it. The Forces called us Headless Families when our men were away, which caused much laughter and not a little indigestion. Who did they think kept homes and families going?

I can't remember whose idea it was, but a lace making group was started and I loved it. We all bought 'Lace Pillows' the proper ones, filled with straw, and lots of bobbins, some of which were beautifully carved, and beads to decorate them with. Living in Forces houses on the camp we all supported and helped each other. Eventually enough lace was made to edge the alter cloth at our church.

Holy Mary Mother of God by Tina Cribbin

I remember Holy Mary mother of god, send me down a couple of bob. That is when she had no Park Drive cigs. I remember her dressed for the pub pan stick with dyed jet-black hair, new false teeth and a red nylon dress. 'Mam, what time are you back?' Well when you are in love you don't feel the cold. She had a saying for everything. Me and our kid used to just sigh at her. If you whistled, it was 'a crowing hen has no luck'?

She had the usual 'you born in a barn', 'what's for dinner Mam?' 'Shit shite and sugar'! Her best was religious, I think being Irish brought out something special, for example when moaning about the auld feller, she would often say 'God forgive me for f**king swearing' and bless herself. When the dementia took hold, it was one of the last things to go. When the priest visited the care home, my mum listened politely but then stood up and told the priest "here you better get lost, I'm no born-again virgin." It was a proud moment. My Mam was still there somewhere. As I write this, I'm getting emotional and I know EXACTLY what she would say... 'What you need is a good dose of salts'. I'm smiling now

Me Julie by Julie Sawdyke and Tina Cribbin

The phoenix of our flats
A beautiful survivor
She will always has your back

A past that was
Painful she spun
Into gold
She holds beauty
Right down to her soul

She spreads her wings
And wraps them tight
Around her family
And those that need

A friend, a hug, or those
Who have a difficult life

Everyone needs a Julie
To have as a friend
Straight up
Straight down
She always defends

Those who face injustice
Those who've just had enough of it.
Her support radiates
Her actions demonstrate
A kindness through and through

There is nothing quite as nice
Sitting with my Julie having a brew
Discussing marks and sparks,
And sparkly shoes.

She lights up when she laughs.
You tell her your problems
She'll say don't be daft
I'll make you a brew

Sit down forget about that
And you do because
That's me Julie
From our flats!!!

My Place by Lil Luckham

My Place was my space, a step as the stairs turned in the house I grew up in, my refuge when the Ma and Da rolled in from the pub, sitting listening, often crying as Mam fought against knowing her place! Confusion my place of many emotions as in they made up the next day... do you know your place Mam; do you want to sit on my step? Change came I grew older, but often I sat in my place and I watched them grow old together with a love many may not understand. They are both gone now and I am back in the home, and I sit in my special place on the step and listen to the walls talking to me...xx

Lonely Proudy by Lil Luckham

My Cabra granny always called me 'lonely proudy' when we visited her, when she sent our medals and shamrock. It was always sent to Teresa, my sister, and 'lonely proudy', nobody has ever heard of this expression so why did she call me that, how did I come across to my lovely rosy cheeked Cabra granny, I never felt lonely or proud but maybe she sensed something in me and when I meet her again she may tell me...I do hope so..

Sad Day by Sally Casey

My granny always called me Sad Day. I think that I must have been a sad and lonely child. I was born with a cleft palate, and even though it was repaired when I was a baby, I was the victim of cruel taunts, not only from my brothers and sisters who threw vicious words at me when we argued, but these vile words followed me all through my young life from playmates, to those who thought that it was great fun to abuse a child with cruel words.

I think that is how I learned how to swear. It was in retaliation for being hurt by people whom I felt neither liked nor loved me. It grew out of my hurt when I grew up, but I never grew out of my swearing habit. I would never ever hurt anyone by throwing a jibe at them about their physical appearance. That is one thing I was careful about all my life.

When you are on your guard against verbal attack, you either attack in return, or you go and cry inwardly, and I did both. Did my granny see in me the hurt that I suffered from that verbal abuse that she could not guard me against? Is that why she always said in a very subdued voice. Come here to me, poor old Sad Day.

Going to see a man about a dog by Anne Finnegan

When my Dad was telling us stories and improbable tales, we would listen eyes bright, tilted faces upward expecting a good ending. Often, they ended in rubbish or mid-sentence much to our annoyance. "What happened?" We would moan. Dad's answer "He fell over a hen and a cock picked him".

To this day we still wonder about that.

Dad where you going?

Going to see a man about a dog.

The Dancing Divil by Anne Finnegan

I was made to stand in front of her. She perched on the edge of the chair. "Put your tongue out till I see if the divil is dancing on it". I couldn't!

I loved Sunday tea homemade apple cakes. Mum would make them after mass on a Sunday morning.

Mm soft, crumbling sweet pastry with tarty stewed apples in the middle and the crust. Oh, the thick crunchy crust!

There were always a few slices left for a cup of tea after the 9 o'clock news. But me having a greedy belly, snuck into the kitchen while all were watching tele, or playing out, and I snaffled the lot. Half a dinner plate of sweet crumbly tarty heaven.

"ANNE come in" mum shouted from the living room, what are you doing? I really tried to eat the rest of the pie as fast I could, but standing there in front of me, mum must have seen the crumbs and the sugar beard that gave me away. The divil was definitely jumping on my tongue as I denied all knowledge of the missing pie.

Sad cake by Emily Oldfield

My grandma used to make this thing called 'Sad Cake' or 'Currant Sad' (not sure if it is a Rossendale dialect thing) which was basically leftover shortcrust pastry gathered together with currants or sultanas, shaped into a round and baked with a milk glaze on. We'd eat it whilst it was still hot from the oven with 'best butter' on, though Grandma always warned us not to eat pastry after 8pm or we would have nightmares. I'm sure that's when she ate the rest!

Army coat blanket by Tina Cribbin

I remember sleeping with Caroline and putting my hands under her arms to get warm. Freezing bony knees and feet despite feeling you were going to suffocate with blankets. And every house seemed to have an army coat! I also remember waking up to my brother's feet in my face as he used to climb in the bottom of the bed at night...yuck!! But I mostly remember our Caroline relaying with relish the latest hammer house of horrors programme to me as she stayed up later. I was terrified!

The Smell of Rubber by Hazel Bedford

This is also a story about bedtime. I remember sleeping with my older and younger sister in a big bed, well it seemed big at the time. One night we had a bad storm, thunder, lightning the lot. I was terrified but did not run into Mum and Dad's room because my older sister put the Eiderdown (I bet you all remember Eiderdowns) up at the window so I could not see the lighting. I don't know why but Dad's overcoat hung on our bedroom door and now I realise it would have been for extra warmth if needed. My Dad worked at Mosley's Rubber Works, it was where the slip road of the Mancunian Way is, off Downing St, near Ardwick Green Park. The only thing is that coat smelt of rubber which became a great comfort to me when he passed away in 1965.

The Shallow end by Lil Luckham

My Dad always talked about sleeping in the same bed with seven brothers, two of them wet the bed, so he always made sure he slept in the shallow end.

The Matriarch by Lil Luckham

From the moment my first sibling was born I was on a losing bet. You are the eldest you should know better, you should show a good example, why, it was my life... trouble and rebellion followed me everywhere and those words haunted me... you are the eldest, the fear of upsetting and disappointing them filled my sack of guilt and Mam's tears when I strayed off the path they chose for me were her own display of sorrow, she was the eldest but did as she was expected to but in later life she described me as her right arm...and told me she was proud of my fighting spirit. I am now the matriarch of my beloved family, still the eldest, still rebelling and bleedin' loving it.

Gran by Sonia James

My gran always called me "my girl" when I was in trouble and with all your memories of sharing beds it brought her to mind. So, this poem isn't about her but reminded me (she and my great gran brought me up Lil) that I didn't have my own bed until I was 12 and she re married.

"Just look at all this mess," Gran said, "that's sand and it's everywhere".
"Just look at you in your dirty clothes, of course you haven't got a care,
And don't you lie to me my girl, I know exactly where you've been".
Now I was in trouble, she'd told me to stay on the village green.
Mum walked in the door and saw gran was cross and unhappy.
Grandma's always cross these days since she 'lost' granddaddy.
If he was lost why couldn't we all just search till we found him
Then bring him home to grandma, make her promise to mind him

Little Sal by Anne Finnegan

I had never been in a place like this; I was about 8. We had driven for a long time I thought. I felt squashed in the back, my arms were sandwiched to my sides and the air was hot. Someone had let off, the acrid smell of Guinness, cabbage & bacon stuck to our noses. We all groaned and tried to reach for an open window. Daddy and the uncles grinned at each other, wearing the Pong like a medal of honour.

We poured out of the charabanc of cars and vans looking down a long wide road flanked on each side with little old looking shops. We walked on grey black cobblestones wet from the rain, uneven, sprawling as far as the road went. We had to step up high to get on to the pavement from the road I was struck at the huge slabs that made the pavement. Mum moved with deliberate memory. I followed the usual "nosey Parker". The door was yellow, a tinkly bell and rattling doorknob introduced us. Her feet moved slowly, gingerly finding the floor. The smell of old wood, sawdust and sweat hovered. I saw a bowed countertop groove lines etched into it. A glass counter housing cakes, and ham and tomatoes. It felt cold and trembling. A big machine that cut ham sat regally on top. The sound of it slicing through a lump of meat carried my eyes to a man with a kind face. "I'm Sally" Mam said "Maisie Fay's daughter"

The man looked at mum for a second, time stopped everything, held in flux. "Ahhhhh Jesus no" said the man breaking into a broad smile revealing great big dentures. "Little Sal" said the man. I thought my Mam's heart might pop out, her smiles were different, I saw her girl face. We were in a small town in Kildare.

Mam, having no mammy of her own, would go there to the aunties for the summer. As a girl she would sit in that shop while her uncle made saddles and did repairs for the riding school.

That day we met old aunties and cousins. We had tea and ham sandwiches in dark dining rooms cakes and biscuits crunched to cooing and Mam's family coming in to say hello and meet us all. It was like the Tom Tom drums were signalling to people little Sal from England had landed. Aunty Mary had run over to cousins who had run up to another aunty and so on. Mam loved that she belonged. Her memories hadn't been dreamt, were real not the books she fed on. Where she sat in her corner near the fire where she hid falling into the stories, away from her many brothers and sisters lost mammy and distant father.

I didn't like the flies being in the dining room hovering high over the ham and tomato treats. The tea was served, in little China cups and everyone was being good.

I remember that good day.

The Confession by Lil Luckham

Strange what runs through run your head when sleep won't come. March 1972 mammy said I had to leave school, no amount of begging or pleading to stay on worked, why did I want to go to college, poor mammy; her lack of aspiration was in the genes, so my life was being mapped out for me. Sister Stella decided that those of us that were leaving should go to a monastery for a few days. Despite their efforts to turns us into ladies we found the local pub and much hilarity was had, not sure if it was worth getting the slipper for but... there was a very handsome young man who had just become a priest and the Thorn Birds syndrome set in. On our return to Manchester we found out he was at a church in Prestwich so off we went, our hearts fluttering. He was doing confessions when we got there so we eagerly waited, my turn came and in I went, my mates say that two minutes later I stormed out shouting "and you can piss off", oh if only I knew what he had said to me.

The Unicorn by Sally Casey

My friend had five children and she had to leave them alone when she went to work.

She was a one parent family and worked extremely hard to keep these children and a home around them. She came home dog tired one day. The oldest boy was that excited that he kept jumping up and trying to tell her his great news.

Now this woman had a mouth like a sewer, and she is shouting at him to calm down and tell her what's going on.

We've got a new pet he says and guess what, it is a UNICORN.

"What the!" She said, what are you talking about.

"We've got a UNICORN," he says, "the only one in the world" says the rag and bone man, I gave him some jumpers and he gave me the Unicorn for them.

"There's no such a thing as an effin' Unicorn," she shouted at him.

All the kids shouted in unison, "it's true Mam, we've got a Unicorn."

"Go and get this F★★★ing Thing and let me see it," she roared.

They all ran out into the yard and dutifully dragged in their new pet, presenting her with their Unicorn.

"That's not a Unicorn," she shouted, "that's an Efffin' GOAT" she said. "Get that F★★★ing Thing out of this house before it starts sh★★ing all over the place. It will eat every bit of clothing that we have. Get it out."

The poor kids were devastated, they cried for hours, the eldest boy was inconsolable. He never forgot that he nearly had the only Unicorn in the world as his pet. I don't know what happened to the goat. The rag and bone man probably got him back and traded him somewhere along the street to some other poor kids looking for an extraordinary pet.

The Hyenas by Anne Finnegan

On a family holiday to Wales when I was 19, we decided to go into Rhyl for the day shopping and mooching. The town was bustling and is extremely hilly. On our travels we came to the foot of a very steep hill. We could see some cute shops and a bank at the top of each other as we looked up and beyond this feckin big hill. With that a voice said "could you help me to the bank" we looked around; the voice came from a rotund lady sitting a wheelchair.

"Oh of course" chirps my mother, "go on Anne, push the lady to the bank" what could I say? I took the handles of the wheelchair and pushed with everything I had. JESUS! she was heavy, 20 stone at least, "F★★★in hell" I gasp as I pushed and pushed her up the hill. All I could hear were screeches of laughter from my sister, mother and cousin as my shoulder pushed against the mighty load, and my arse stuck out the other end. As we finally came to a stop outside the bank yer woman jumps out of the chair and toddles into the bank without a thank, kiss me arse, or nothing. I picked my jaw up from the floor and walked down the hill knackered, to meet the hyenas below.

Angel with Dirty Faces by Lil Luckham

An angel with a dirty face, could be my brother Robert. Such a lovely little lad who quickly became mammy's Blue-eyed boy, if only she knew then the bitterness and resentment it would cause. Me and Teresa welcomed him even though we couldn't watch the end of *Bonanza* as the midwife sent us packing. We loved wheeling him around Ardwick and bringing him home caked in muck, and my relationship with our kid is lasting and enduring. But... 5 years after he was born the youngest came along and a bond was never formed because the 'Blue eyed boy' was viewed as the enemy... sibling rivalry is I believe natural but this was different and to the rest of us hard to understand, 50 years later there is still very little love between them and I have given up being the go-between, our dirty faced angel has never understood it but knows that for some of us he is still our 'Blue eyed boy'

The Mirror Talked Back by Joana Salles

I waited. One of the longest waits of my life. And then the pain came. The most excruciating pain I have ever been in. It took me back to the comfort of my room. I was obsessed with food stuck in my teeth, constantly looking at myself in the mirror. Looking for approval. I asked, 'Mirror, mirror, am I the prettiest yet?'. But he never answered. One day, I heard him talk back to me. He was mumbling meaningless words, one after the other. Each felt like a sword stabbing my scar less skin. You're not thin enough. Your eyes are not big enough. Your mouth is fair enough. You're not perfect enough. So I changed. I ate less, exercised more. But the mirror kept talking. Your thighs are too big. Maybe wear a wig. You cannot wear that to a gig. So, I thought, that mirror must be broken. But every mirror I encountered kept talking back. All the voices would resonate, and I wondered if it was to do with my weight. But after that day, when the pain finally went away, nothing was the same. The next morning, the mirror stopped talking. And there I was wishing he would say something, anything. Instead, I met a different voice, the one in my head.

Three Generations by Sally Casey

I am the littlest one at the back, my Da is wearing the grey suit, my Granda is the other one. He has come to stay with us for a few weeks because granny is in hospital. Granny is lovely, she is very squishy when she gives a hug. She smells like nice soap, and she always has sweets in her apron pocket. Granda is nice as well, but he smells of that stuff that he sniffs up his nose. I think it is called snuff. I don't like the feel of Granda's jacket either, it's very rough, and I do be raging when he ruffles my hair like I am a baby.

I am a big boy now, Ma said I could go on the walk with Da and Granda, but I was not to talk, because they had a lot to tell each other. And if I got in the way I wouldn't be let go with them until I learnt some manners.

Well here I am just following them. I think that I am being a good boy. Just look at the way I am able to keep up with them as they walk down to the park. I am big enough now to fold my arms around my back just like them. I could not do that if I wasn't a big boy, could I.

I'm nearly two and a half now, and soon I'll be three. When I am four, I will be able to go to school with my big brother who is nearly six. Mam said that I have more sense than him, he is always getting into trouble. He gets lots of smacks from Mam, and he is always sent to bed without cocoa and toast. I always get my cocoa, I really like it at bed time. It is so nice.

My brother says that I get to go out with Da too

many times. He will pinch me on the arms tonight when we go to bed as punishment because he was not allowed to come with us.

Aw well, I'm going to try and keep up with them, although my legs and my arms are getting heavy. It's hard being a big boy. I'm going to ask Da to put me up on his shoulders for a while. I don't think he will call me a sissy. Do You?

Alf by Sonia James

Alf had been made foreman at the works. To celebrate he had bought himself a new cap and a pair of proper bicycle clips; all black, shiny and proper as befit his new station in life. Old string that had been good enough until now is thrown in the bin. He was looking forward to his new position as he cycled along his usual route. The roads were so much busier now that most of the men took this short cut, not much more than a lane really passed open fields.

But this morning he was astonished to see someone, or more likely a crew, had built a high fence all along the fields edge. Maybe they are going to put horses or cattle in there. Oh don't tell me they're going to build more flats he thought. Now Alf was quite a tall man but even on his bike he couldn't see over the top of it. He was never late for work, but curiosity got the better of him and he couldn't resist. Leaning his bike against the fence he climbed up onto its cross bar and looked over. Empty field, same long grass, same trees, no, wait, these shimmered, a bit like Silver Birch. What? No it must be the angle of the early morning sun giving them an ethereal look. Strange. No wind, tall grass and tree leaves perfectly still, he scanned the area. Apart from the trees it all looked the same. and then no, wait, he saw what looked like a child's swing hanging motionless from one of the lowest branches.

Alf's cap lifted as he scratched his head. He looked around the field again. Same shiny trees swing still there but looking to the left a bit he frowned. He blinked but suddenly saw three old fashioned, very ornate dining chairs in a semi-circle facing towards him. They weren't there just now. Was someone playing tricks? His stomach flip flopped, and he jumped down from his cross bar, sat down with a bump, grabbed his new cap from his head and bit down hard on the soft crown.

"Morning Alf, what's to do. Don't tell me you fell off your bike". It was Tom, on his way to work. Alf looked quite strange as he looked up at him but for an answer, he just shook his head pushed his thumb over his shoulder. "What am I looking at?" Tom asked. Alf just shook his head and kept his thumb pointing over his shoulder but managed to whisper, "Over the fence Tom, look over the fence". "What fence man, what fence you talking about". Alf stared up at Tom then risked a glance over his shoulder, and fainted! 'By heck' thought Tom, 'if promotion turns you daft I'll stay as I am thank you very much' and emptied his water bottle over Alf's head.

Heartache by Sonia James

His eyes no longer meet mine
But I'll bury my head, pretend it's all fine
He no longer wants to hold my hand
Or dance along to his favourite band
Did he just get bored? Or did he meet another?
He's become a mystery and I want to smother
These feelings I have, fear, pain, doubt

If I had courage I'd ask him straight out
Afraid though of the answer he'll give
I wonder is this how other couples live?
So it looks like I'm stuck with the status quo
But my heart is breaking and I want him to know

What Shall I Do Today? by Sally Casey

Maybe I'll stay in bed
No, that is not being positive
The negativity will drive me mad.

I'm being as good as I can be
No moaning, and no swearing
Am I getting used to this isolation?
Or am I beyond caring.

I thought my days would be too long
How wrong have I been?
I'm on the go from 9 -5
No, it hasn't been a dream

Plants planted; bushes clipped
Dried leaves binned; flags swept.
Washing dried, more tomorrow
In former times I would have wept.

Thank god it is spring, and hadn't he been generous,
Sun shining, heat so very soothing
Is this the sign we needed, to slow us all down?
I hope that I will remember it,
When next my brow needs smoothing

Actions Don't Always Speak Louder by Sonia James

He was a shy technology magician.
Smiling shyly, shifting position
Pulling her skirt down over her knees
Face hidden by hair, she just said, "please".
He pulled a face, but really he knew
He'd help her, she hadn't a clue.
His heart beat to match hers every day,
He loved her, but what could he say?
He opened his mouth breathed in, but,
Just passed back her laptop, closing it shut
If only he had looked into her eyes
He'd see her love, she couldn't disguise.
The moral here is as clear as a shout
If you don't speak up, you are bound to miss out

Steps to Heaven by Tina Cribbin

Be brave I tell myself as put my foot encased in years old slipper on the first step. Yes, the first thing I remember was when he asked me to dance, he made me swoon with his confident manner and his articulate way of speaking. He was different from the other lads round here. He had plans. By the second step we were courting, and his confident manner became arrogance and control. But still I stayed, I was young, all the girls wanted him, I thought that's how men should be strong and masterful.

The third step was most frightening. I was going to have a baby. I'm too afraid to tell anyone. On the third step I learned isolation and secrets. Secret bruises and slaps, sharp words that scar. Just as I landed on the fourth step, I told him when he came in drunk and was lifting his heavy work boot over me I screamed "I'm pregnant!"Sobbing and sniffles, huddled up tight in the corner of the kitchen... wait.

On the fifth step I learned about forgiveness and promises, I had never seen a grown man cry. He told me all the ways he got it wrong and all the ways I could make it right.

On the sixth step I learned about keeping quiet, the house spick and span, food on the table, no moaning. It was time for the 7th step the birth of our son. I could do no wrong. On the 7th step I learned about failed promises as I left the hospital with hidden finger bruises.

By step eight I was a professional caricature of any version of me he wanted, the real me left years ago. I stay because of my son. On step 8 I learned patience. My time will come.

Step nine and the noose is tighter, I no longer work or have friends. I no longer leave the house. Our Jack gets me stuff in on the way home from school. He's good like that, he doesn't tell his Dad, especially as Dad now spends most money and time in the pub. As I spend time alone on step nine, I learn about planning a way out.

Step ten I am outside the monster's lair. I hear the snores brought on from alcohol and sleeping tablets snuck into half-opened cans that he would finish regardless of how long they had been there. I get the pillow and cover his beer swollen face, and I press for all the steps I had to take, and for waiting so long for the courage to do it. At last all was calm. I tidied the room. I began my descent.

Step one going down I learned about my skill as an actress he taught me well. By the bottom of the stairs I learned to laugh loudly....

What Writing Means to Me by Joana Salles

I joined this writing group a couple of months ago. To this day, I'm not quite sure why. I never thought writing was for me. Either academically or creatively I don't think I've ever been really good at it. But when I met Tina, I realised that every random activity is made of amazing and joyful people. And that is why it's worth trying them out. But one day I knew. I knew it was for me because of how amazing it made me feel when I finally managed to put words on the paper, read them out loud and genuinely felt proud of myself. Not necessarily for the beauty of what I had written but for the feeling of sharing and being seen and heard. That's when I realised that writing had always been around me. My first love was born through writing. It was non-existent in the real world but putting words together on a piece of paper made it feel real.

When my grandmother died it wasn't real either. Not until I put words on it. Set it on the paper and acknowledge how it made me feel. Some may say feelings are not real until talked about, well I would say feelings are not real until you share them, and what a medium to share them through writing. My grandmother wrote something every single day of her life, sometimes just to talk about the weather, other times to put words on how her miscarriage made her feel. When she died and we emptied her house, we got to read some of it. Through her journal, she left something priceless, pieces of her mind and bits of her life. I guess in a way maybe that's why I joined this writing group. They somehow remind me of her. Of how joyful and happy she used to be. But, also of how much she struggled on her own. I wish she could have found such a group to support her through the bad times and the worse ones.

Writing is like therapy for me, and I'm sure it could have been for her. I've found it to be the best medium for me to express myself. To tell myself things that my brain has buried, but also to share my struggle with others, to tell the world that they are not alone. Words are empowering. Words empower me. And I'm sure words empower you. Words empower communities. Words are what make us unique as a species. Otherwise we would just be talking monkeys. And maybe we still are. Writing doesn't matter. What matters is what you say. What matters is how you say it. The word you choose to use. What matters is who you share it with. What matters is the impact it has. What matters is how it makes you feel. What matters is the bond that emerges from it. Writing allows us to be a part of something bigger. Writing has allowed me to become my better self. Writing doesn't mean anything to me, it means everything.

My Favourite Place In The World by Sally Casey

I have many favourite places in the world that I have visited, New York, Miami, Florida, Spain, Paris, Rome, and many more that I have loved being in. I do not have to go back extremely far in my memory to recall the best place, that I can call my very own Favourite.

It is situated in North County Dublin, a coastal town called Rush. When we first started visiting this pretty little place there were only a few shops on the main street, including a chip shop that was very popular, there was probably ten pubs, a Catholic church, the beach of course, and the harbour. The main street was called the village then, now it is known as the town. Over the years it has also acquired a Tesco store, a Theatre, beautiful brand new town houses, and is now the place to live in, that's if you are a well-paid professional person who can afford to buy a property in this very lively lovely place.

Back in the summer of the seventies and eighties when we were on our annual two weeks holiday in Dublin, my in laws would loan us a small caravan ,or a static mobile home which they owned in Rush, which was about twenty miles outside of Dublin. These little holiday homes were situated in a caravan park which was actually a field where the farmers once grew potatoes.

The potato furrows were still in the ground, and you had to be careful where you were walking, or you would go over very quickly on your ankle, especially if you had a few drinks in you.

There was a little shed with a couple of sinks to wash yourself, and a couple of toilets also. These were known as the washrooms. Nothing bijou there, cold running water, not hot, but you didn't ask for more, you accepted what was there, and were glad of it. We knew no better in them days.

It was never a freebie when I was offered the loan of a caravan or a static home to spend a week or so in with my family. They would throw in at least two of their children for me to take to Rush, and the kids would be told, now be good for Sally, which they really were, so along with my four and Dad and I off we trucked to Rush for a week. The caravan was a four berth one, the static mobile slept six. They both had a double bed in a little bedroom, but we only ever got a loan of one of them, so we had to be grateful for whichever one was free that week. Me and Dad slept in the bedroom, our youngest child slept with us, and the other five or six children, depending on how many were there with us, all slept in what was the sitting room, taking turns to sleep on the long seats, or lying on the floor in sleeping bags. I never heard one of them children complain about the sleeping arrangements. They were happy to be by the seaside with their cousins.

Cooking meals for eight or nine people on a stove with two Calor gas rings was a work of art. We just got on with it, and if their bellies were full, the kids, all six or seven of them, were gone like lightening to the beach each morning where they spent hours and hours enjoying themselves.

I would cook a big Sunday dinner for us all, and the bigger children would be sent off to the fields to pull big heads of cabbage to be cooked with a big piece of ham, and big floury potatoes.

One morning I made a big trifle for Sunday dessert, and as there was no fridge I balanced it on the window ledge to let it set. All was going well until some visitors from Dublin, out for a Sunday drive, called in on us. One of their kids kept jumping on and off the step, and the trifle fell off the window sill and splattered everywhere. Was I angry, Yes I was. They had only come down because they thought that they would get a free meal from us. They had little chance of a free meal after that performance by their child!

We always kept our youngest one with us as he was a toddler, but at night Dad took them all off again to the beach, and they would go off to the rock pools catching crabs and digging up cockles and winkles. Football, cricket, rounders, swimming, my kids had a ball, no ice cream men on the beach, no funfair either, they just made their own fun, and enjoyed it all.

Me and Dad used to go down to the village for a drink at about ten at night, with the promise to them all of chips on our way home, (bribery,) which worked every night.

We went to Skerries a few times in the evenings. Skerries was about ten minutes away by bus, another beautiful fishing village, to watch the fishermen bring in their catch, which was so exciting. They may throw a few fish to you for free, if they had had a good catch and were feeling generous.

The men could have been out at sea fishing for two or three days and nights. They worked extremely hard for their living, and you could see how exhausted they were coming off the boats.

I would store the fish under the caravan in cold water overnight and fry up the fish next day. Delicious fresh fish straight from the sea.

I do not remember it ever raining down there, it probably did but it didn't seem to matter to the kids. I don't know what we would have done if it did bucket down rain every day, there was nowhere to go, there was nothing to do, and how long could the kids be entertained in a little caravan with a deck of cards and a ten inch television.

We packed up early once and returned to Dublin, because we had been warned that a storm was imminent and would be a bad one. It didn't materialise, and I was so angry with myself for bringing everyone away from their bit of paradise, I promised myself that I would think twice in future before being so hasty.

One of my girls met her first boyfriend down in Rush, a holiday romance. We lost the youngest one in

Skerries one Sunday morning. We were all at mass and he was being looked after by a family member in his car. He was so engrossed in reading his Sunday paper that he didn't see the child climb out of the car window and go walkabout. The child was not missed until we came back to the car. Imagine what it was like trying to find a missing three-year-old child with hundreds of people coming out of Mass. We eventually found him when someone remembered seeing a child wearing a tee shirt with a union jack on the front, so child found, drama over.

We had many very enjoyable holidays in Rush on our annual trip to Dublin. To this day, if anyone asks my family, who are all grown up now with their own families about summers by the sea, without a doubt every one of them will all chime in and talk over each other, reminiscing about their wonderful days in Rush by the sea.

What makes it such a special place for me is the wonderful memories that I have of how happy we all were down there in Rush. My children were happy and healthy, and they were with their cousins whom they loved. We had huge extended families that we met up with and enjoyed their company. I was incredibly happy also, there was nothing else that I could wish for, and I so enjoyed watching my family relax and know that I was the one who made it come true for them.

Those summers set us up for the cold winter back in Manchester, but we knew that come next summer, there was the chance that we might be once again offered a four berth caravan, or a six berth luxury mobile home where we would all pile in and enjoy another magical weeks holiday at very little expense in the most beautiful place on earth.

Mam by Tina Cribbin

I promised myself all the ways
I would do life differently to HER
I would never make the same mistakes,
I would be kinder, wiser and stronger.

I would not let any monsters in
I wouldn't lose my heart in a bottle of gin
I would not look defeated,
Worn out with the same mistakes
Any dreams that were held
Had long retreated

She was easy to judge
She got it all wrong
When everyone else got it right

I hoped for a different mother
A different life
Through slammed doors
And the all-knowing
Teenage knowledge
My words cut deep
As I pulled out the knife

I began to make mistakes of my own
Found the monsters who tried to control
I made mistakes in life that left me crushed
The people I should of loved
I just pushed

When lay alone in bed at night
I realised all the ways my mother
Got it right

Loving through the impossible
Believing the improbable
Her forgiveness towards me unstoppable

She knew that life can't be frozen
Freeze framed into a perfect Photograph
Understood that life takes us
Down stormy difficult paths

Her loving and loving and loving
Was all she had to give
Not a penny in her pocket
But she gave all she had To her kids

Born of the black bog dust
Watching her dreams turn to rust
Missed opportunities that
Got lost in the in the weekend wash

Encased by grace
A fragile life
Lived on tough estates
But she didn't hesitate
When it came to me

Am I like my mother?
I really hope to be
An angel born with dirty wings

We are all flawed
Beautiful people
And that is exactly
How it's meant to be

<u>My Perfect Dreamboat by Sally Casey</u>

Would be a guy of about forty-five to fifty years old, about five foot ten to six feet tall. It does not matter if he is a little shorter, but I do not want a little fella. He can have the looks of Kenny Dalglish, the ex-footballer. I spotted Kenny once on Market Street with his wife, and I really wanted to follow him, not her. He was dressed in a fabulous camel coloured Crombie overcoat, and he was wearing a beautiful pair of brown leather shoes. His hair was slicked back, you know, the kind of hair that you want to run your fingers through whilst you are doing something else with him. I cannot remember what else he wore, but what I was looking at was enough to get my juices flowing. I did follow them into the store, but they were only shopping for food, I wished they were going to the men's deptartment, but no, who wants to see a fine thing like him squeezing ripe tomatoes and pears. There was a lot more he could have been squeezing if you get my meaning.

Well, to get back to my dream boat. I have been looking and dreaming of him for many years. Where is he? He cannot be that hard to find. I am not asking for much, well maybe a little more than I should be looking for, but I am entitled to search for my dream. I am entitled to, and I will not be put off, thank you very much.

He really needs to have money, well, I do not want a guy without means, I want to respect him, and I am not going to do that if he is broke. Anyone can find a poor man, not me. Now, if he had a nice big house, and a nice sleek car, that would be a bonus, and how happy that would make me. I believe that I deserve that much.

Did I mention good looks, I do love a man who is good looking, and is full of confidence. He must be a snazzy dresser also; I cannot abide a man who does not wear a decent set of clothes.

Now, you may think that I have set my sights extremely high, but I will disagree with you there. Just look at what he will be getting. He will be getting me, Perfect little me. I am what he has been looking for all of his life, he may not recognise it, but believe me, when he sets his eyes on me, he will know for sure that I am the dream that he has been having all of his adult life.

Dreams are what we are made of, and I will continue wishing and hoping that my dream comes through, and that my dreamboat finds me, or better still, let me find him, and I will make both of our lives the dreamiest ever and ever and ever.

Thespia in Trouble by Allison Forbes

Thespia shrank into the dark corner she had found herself and tried to stop shaking. She was more frightened than she could ever remember; even as a small kitten, and she had been a very small kitten, the last to be born and not expected to live, she had not experienced terror like this. She tried to remember how it had come about.

She had been reclining at ease outside the theatre in a welcome patch of sun. It had been raining, on and off, for most of the week, and as it was now spring the heating in the building had been switched off. Somehow, she was not sure how it had happened, let alone why, she had been swept up and bundled unceremoniously into a motor vehicle. Since she had never in her life been in any kind of car she was completely bewildered. She was swaddled in material and could only see part of the interior, and nothing at all the outside world. It was noisy, smelly, and very, very frightening.

Gradually, as nothing worse seemed to be happening, she began to lose some of her fear and felt it being replaced, first by anger, and then by outrage. How could this be allowed to happen? How could this happen to Her? As time passed, she drew the rage round her like a blanket, bringing back her natural courage.

At last, after what felt like hours, and when the courage was beginning to seep out through her paws, the vehicle stopped. Still wrapped in the folds of material she was, further indignity, stuffed into a bag. She heard a strange sound running along the opening and enclosing her. She had been zipped into the bag but had no means of knowing it.

Footsteps, she was moving, though goodness alone knew where. More strange sounds, and smells; she felt she was surrounded by people. She yowled as loud as she could, but nobody seemed to notice. The sound of the footsteps changed from time to time; the feet were moving over different surfaces. Finally, after the last sounds, where the feet seemed to be moving over a hollow bridge, she felt herself being dumped, ungently, on the floor and pushed, where she had no idea. There was still a lot of noise and confusion but at least she was stationary.

Greatly daring, having managed to fight her way out of the swaddling material, Thespia lifted a paw up to the top of the bag that contained her. A claw, extended to its farthest, hooked into something and she pulled. Joy of joys, the bag, she now realised that it was a bag, opened. Cautiously she peered out. Gracious, what a lot of feet! She had never seen so many. Still, she was tucked into corner and felt safe enough, being black helped. She climbed out of the constricting bag and crouched in her dark corner, waiting to see what would happen next.

What happened was indeed even more terrifying. Incredible noise assaulted her outraged ears, the world dashed into frenzied movement, then a strange sensation, almost of weightlessness bewildered her even more.

WHAT WAS GOING ON?

Far below, on earth that stayed where it should, Angel gazed up at the azure sky at the vapour trail that crossed it. Idly she wondered where the plane was going, and who was on it. She hoped they were enjoying their flight.

Had Angel known it, Thespia was not enjoying her flight; she neither knew nor cared whether the owners of all those feet were happy or not. Nor did she know that she was, in fact, even on an aircraft, let alone why all these strange events were happening.

Gradually she began to feel less terrified. The noise died down, nobody disturbed her in her dark corner, and she was quite comfortable. She was, had she realised it, fortunate in that the seat under which she was crouching was unoccupied or she might have been discovered.

Time passed, and as nothing alarming had occurred Thespia decided that it was time she explored her surroundings. In the distance she could hear some shouting, but nothing was moving near her; indeed, it seemed to be almost unnaturally still, being as how humans were involved. In her experience human beings seemed to need to be constantly on the move. She crept out, pausing with just her head exposed, and looked to her left: nothing. She crept a little further forward and looked to her right.

Horror! A pair of feet, exceptionally large and moving very fast, were charging down on her. In a panic, instead of retreating into her hiding place Thespia leapt forward. Instant uproar! The feet collided with her – inflicting a nasty bruise, though Thespia did not discover this until sometime later – a heavy body landed on her, depriving her briefly of breath, though very soon she was able to yowl at full pitch of her powerful lungs and claw herself free.

"Catch that man!"

"Careful, he's got a gun!"

"Get the gun!"

"Where did that cat come from?"

"Sit down, everybody, we've got the man, the danger's over. What cat? I can't see any cats."

Thespia, wisely, had returned to her hiding place.

"She tripped him up and saved us!"

"How do you know it's she? Here, kitty, kitty."

Suddenly Thespia heard a voice that she knew. She crept out again and slunk towards it. She looked up; could it be? Was it? It was! With an ear-splitting howl of delight and relief she swarmed upwards and dug all her claws into the chest of Tom from the theatre.

"What the dickens," said her astonished saviour, staggering slightly, and wishing that cats did not have quite so many claws. "Thespia? It cannot be. What are you doing here, for goodness' sake?" Thespia purred franticly and hung on.

"She saved our lives," said a tearful woman, wondering if she could stroke the cat, and deciding that it would be unwise. She did seem to have a large number of claws, and probably teeth too.

At this point one of the cabin crew, who had taken

a moment to make sure that she presented a suitably pristine appearance, decided it was time to take control.

"It's all over," she said reassuringly. "We have the man tied up and we'll be landing shortly at an RAF base. Please return to your seats. We have had quite enough drama for one flight, don't you think?" The passengers grinned sheepishly and shuffled back to their places. "The cat is she yours?" she asked Tom disapprovingly.

"Not exactly, she belongs to the theatre where I work," Tom replied. "I can't imagine how she got here, though it's a good thing she did as it turned out. Was that man trying to hijack the plane?"

"It looks like it," the girl agreed. "Can you take charge of her? Fortunately, we haven't left UK airspace and will be landing in the UK so with luck there won't be any quarantine problems."

"Of course, I'll take care of her. Look, there's a bag under that seat. Do you think she was in that?"

"Possibly. She can go back in it anyway."

So Thespia, protesting loudly, was incarcerated once again.

She was mollified a few days later when Angel showed her a handsome newspaper photograph of herself apparently holding court when the plane landed at the air force base.

"You're a heroine," Angel told her. Thespia looked smug and turned her attention to her food bowl.

She never did find out why she had been abducted in the first place.

My Favourite Place in The World by Sonia James

My favourite place in the world
And I don't care if you think it absurd
It was when we lived in North Wales
And from my eyes dropped a lifetime of scales
The first time I entered an aromatic stable
I wanted to ride a horse, but I was not able
So, the first thing I did was take lessons
A serious business no messin'
Every week for two hours
All I was taught I devoured
I was taught a lot of what she knew
And after we'd talk and share a brew
She taught me to be brave and to jump
Many a time I fell off with a bump
"Up you get" she'd say, no sympathy here
She'd oft say it loud for everyone to hear
But we all would have ridden through fire for her
Afraid of her ire, don't be absurd
Our strength and safety were her main concern
And after a while it worked. I did learn.

Anarchist Jumpers by Tina Cribbin

You preach about food waste
As food bank food
Leaves a bad taste,
In your mouth

Not quite ethical enough
But we can't afford your unicorn prices.
But thanks for the heads up

Evicted lives

A Great Big Dollop of Hope

Become
Works of art
For urban entrepreneurs
With city street smarts

Bearded men at artisan markets Selling poor people lives
While shouting
They are Marxists

Capitalist in anarchists jumpers you may look the part
love
But we all have your number

Photographers
Soundscape artists,
The creative revolution
Look what you have started.

Humanity departed forget about social change.
You've become chained in the game of social gaze

Watching communities and lives turning to dust.
Whilst you listen, picture and pretend you are one of us.

You're just a capitalist dressed as anarchist
Determined to make a buck.

Change your viewing
Turn back the clock
Rewind your moral compass
Turn your head
From your capital
And stock

Stop making a living
Out of our lives while you watch
Our pain turn into your wealth.

Clicking cameras and recorders into my face actually is
of no help

Capitalist in anarchists jumpers
Where will you be
When my going gets tough...

Speaking at meetings about community change
As the change in your profit pocket weighs heavy
You front it out
With eloquent words

Deflecting the blame
No time for
Self-reflection
Or shame in your world
You simply concentrate
On the notes that unfurl

Into your anarchist
Bank balance

A Foursome by Sonia James

In my teenage years, a foursome was like a safety net
You might only have met him at a dance, so you did not
know him yet.
A friend would bring her boyfriend, maybe we would
meet at the park
One I remember was just daft like me, so we all made
for the kiddie's part
Being whizzed around giddily fast on the roundabout
The two lads laughing at our squeals gave each other
that friendly arm clout
As all went well, he walked me home and we kissed at

the garden gate
Oh yes, I liked this one a lot, and couldn't wait for our next date.

Friendship by Sonia James

Friendship is a magical thing, hold onto it with both hands.
That tie that runs between you helps when you are lost in those bad lands.
The darkness will try to engulf you but there is always help near by,
Reach out, hold on, there's someone there who will catch your sigh.

And friendship is reciprocal, one day they might need you,
Then you can hold your hand out, have a chat, give a shoulder, share a brew.
So, when your hour is darkest and you're in the slough of despond,
Remember, hold your hand out, someone will always respond.

Second-hand Rose By Sonia James

If you like you can call me second hand Rose
I love charity shops it's where I buy my clothes
"Waste not want not, make do and mend," my Gran used to say
If she knows what's happening now, she'll be turning in her grave.
Just look at the rubbish that is dropped in our streets
Beer cans, plastic bottles and wrappers from sweets
We've a beautiful planet but we are killing it dead

Why can't we be thoughtful and careful instead
But we want what we want and we buy it every day
Now look at our world and see how we pay
When they looked back at Earth, they could see the scars
But never mind, do not worry, we'll all go and live on Mars

Love by Sonia James

He was just turned ninety, she was eighty-nine
Seventy years together a long life not always fine
Every day they called in to our shop on the corner
My Dad, who is nearly their age no longer called a foreigner
They always come in together, he always opened the door
Then they look around in wonder like they had never been in before
Then off they would go again, chatting all the while
She would look at him, and in her eyes, you could see her smile
After seventy years together still lots to say to each other
There was just the two of them, no children, sister or brother
And as they walked away you could see their love wrapped around each other

A Parallel Universe by Hazel Bedford

As we look around our small part of this large world, it seems we have stumbled into some strange replica of our world that is lacking People, because of social isolation. You could say a parallel universe. At times it seems daunting but all we need to do is open our eyes to the wonders that are unfolding.

Nature is carrying on as it normally would. We only need to stop and listen to the wonderful birdsong, the hive of activity as they are preparing to mate. It's wonderful to hear, they are busy making their nests in readiness.

The gardens are springing into life; flowers, shrubs, bushes and trees.

The time for farmers is a busy one. New life appearing with the lambs, calves and all farm animals. Not forgetting all the crops, they will be growing.

This of course must send a message to us "if we care to stop and listen". It tells us that there is light in the dark place we are in now. All we have to do is stay strong, stay safe and take care.

A Walk in the Park by Anne Finnegan

I walked to Platt Fields Park in the rain today. Hood up, hands dug deep into my pockets. Drip drop drip drip drop on my hood, a quiet reminder of nature and me. I can hear my breathing through my walking silence, a rhythm begins the happen.

Walking breathing dripping.
Walking breathing dripping.
Walking breathing dripping.

My mind turns over, my feet one in front of another. Twigs, leaves, mud make their own sounds under my feet.

The park empty, the green grass vivid and singing its way in spring.

It calms and soothes me, walking through the trees Their leaves fluttering in the breeze hanging heavy sodden from the rain. Hanging branches hug me, the lake lay still but said hello again.

Ducks, birds, swans, look at me with expressions to say "Oh it's you" they look away uninterested but welcoming. How they welcome me with no strings attached.

I leave feeling cleansed and calm.

Wet ankles along the bottom of my jeans. I Feel sleepy and warm.

Ours Was Just an Ordinary Group Hazel Bedford

A group of young people who belonged to a Youth Club at their local Methodist Church. They were fortunate enough to live at a time when there was plenty of work around, so they were in employment and earning money. This group decided they would give some of their money every month (anonymously). They were encouraged to do this by their Church Minister and the Youth Club Leader.

Each were given envelopes with their own number on so they could put their contribution in. They also did fund raising projects. The group decided which projects they would do.

Some of the projects were: -

Underprivileged children taken out to the seaside, with packed lunches etc. Children from Manchester and Salford.

Decorated a house in Oldham.

Sent money to India to have a Well dug in a village.

And lots of other things as well.

Ours was just an ordinary group.

She Rode her High Horse by Hazel Bedford

Who did she think she was, she had only been here for a short time? And here she was throwing her weight about calling the shots.

She had moved to our town not that long ago, from the country. Annabel had volunteered to join our Town's Summer Fête committee.

What did she know how our Fête works, as it would be so different from a Country Fête? But no, it seems that she who shouts loudest gets her own way. She knew what buttons to press as well. So outvoted – Annabel got her way on how this Fête would be run.

So came the day of the Fête – so all the adulation given to Annabel " SHE RODE HER HIGH HORSE ALL OVER THE TOWN"

She Rode Her High Horse by Sally Casey

The Witch, she thought that she was the queen of the May, but she was only the cart behind the Donkey.

I'm telling you, when that one got her white stilettos on at night and her red dress that was a size too tight for her, well, all I'll say was there wasn't a decent man in the town who would give her a second look. Others did of course, but that lot had no finesse at all.

As the women at the wash house called her she was anything but a lady, but did she care. No she did not. She was a disgrace.

She rode her high horse all over town. She strutted into the clubs at night and never had to pay an entrance fee. Fellas fell over themselves to buy her a drink. She could order anything, and they just paid up, grateful for a thank you from her. Some say she was extremely attractive, but I never thought that she was anything out of the ordinary. She didn't have a job at the mill, or anywhere that employed decent women, so you can imagine how she made a living.

I saw my fella eyeing her up last Saturday while I was queueing at the butchers for some tripe for his tea, I said, "if you want to wear this tripe, keep staring at that tramp".

"I never looked at her," he said.

"Good," I said.

Well, all I'm saying is, how come she is so popular, and here am I. I hate her, I really do, but sometimes I just wish that I were her if only for a few hours. Isn't it dreadful that I'm jealous of that woman who struts around as if she was the jockey who won the Grand National and was leading the winner into the paddock.

The Horse Trotted Back to Banbury Cross by Sonia James

Her childhood accounted for her growing up insecure
To avoid hurt she stayed in her house, and closed the door
But she really loved to write, and she learned to draw
But her prolific offerings made some other people sore
So, she made the decision not to do either anymore
She stayed in her house and again locked the door
Then a neighbour needed help, she'd always been quite poor
When admitting she needed help she ached to the core
With courage in her hands that were old and quite sore
She knew who to call on she had been there before
But the door that she knocked on stayed shut fast, no help there anymore
Then she heard hooves stomping and opened the stable

door
And the horse trotted back to Banbury Cross
Where he had lived in the days of yore

He was less than himself by Anne Finnegan

Once an upstanding staunch man,
Big hard-working hands, large shoulders
And a shy smile.
Definite standards, no means no

How can this tumble to ashes on the ground?
Because you're strong, you can't be weak
Because you're working… just speak
Because you're sad… you just act out

You hide, you punch
You blunder and hurt.
You don't know how to say
Help me
Soothe me
Support me
Understand me

Instead you hide behind your staff
You brushed me away
With the ashes on the ground

No woman is an island. Or are they? Anne Finnegan
Being an island means being surrounded by water
Living alone means nothing and no one can get to you.
You are central-still-one

Sometimes I feel like that, still amongst the speed of life
around me, standing on my island separate but viewing
all
Being on an island can be good you get to stop the tide

coming in but then no one goes, weeds start to grow around my feet
I begin to take root.
Sometimes I rip my feet from the ground carefully and giant stride to the shore, wade in and begin to tread the water

But I am not a good swimmer I turn back and fight back to the shore
I am an island
I am one.

The Pieces of Me by Hazel Bedford

I am divided into pieces, some large and some small, as I follow life's path. Am I divided or am I torn into pieces because they both mean different things to me. I think I will go with divided; it doesn't seem as harsh. Like most people these pieces will cover a whole lot of ground.

The pieces of me, family takes a huge chunk – I've decided I like the word chunk very much. So, as I said family takes a huge chunk, and of course friends take another large chunk. I try to keep the smaller chunks to the things that sadden me, although that's not always an easy thing to do. Things that make me happy also take a huge chunk, like all the nature we can appreciate at this difficult time. I didn't realise just how much of my piece's or chunks contain lots and lots of love.

This is me and I hope people don't mind me changing pieces to CHUNKS.

A chunk You Say? by Anne Finnegan

I'm definitely a chunk kind of girl.
I have a chunky mid-riff and a chunky heart.
Some bits have been shaved off and whittled into

interesting shapes.

Some have definite arrow points that prick at me, others have curvy edges and secret hideaways housing so many colours and doorways leading to a superhighway to different lands.

Some doorways call loud, some echo, lots slam.

Shiny door handles, big booming metal knockers, handles bright, rusty – dusty – stiff old from misuse some groovy n moody stylish & cool. Most aging and raging at not being opened.

A little creaking wooden door slightly ajar creaking a promise? Dare I press on?

Next Corpse Arriving by Tina Cribbin

It's a war out here
It's a war

When your life is measured for simply having
The pleasure of being born on the wrong side of class

When your life is deemed unviable and void
Your dreams thrown out with the rubbish
All the hope and the love in your heart destroyed

She tasted the words they gave her
And she smelled the hate they gave
She touched the disgust, in the report
And heard the sounds of the chains

To be disabled in world where no one can see it
And you have to prove your pain.
They don't believe the doctors
Her body now inked with the shame

They break her down slowly through
Scripted questions intent on abuse.

They tell her they are on her side
As they silently pass to her the ready-made noose.
How many ways can she crumble?
How many ways to die
How many ways to kill her
Her only escape from austerities tyrannical lies

So she takes the noose you gave her
It's not sanctioned or comes with a loan.
The government give them freely as they show you the
way home

And the roads are all littered with corpses
The disabled, the poor and the old,
The genocide of this government for those
Who didn't make the disability threshold

And the government say we are winning
And the papers spin their lies.
She now stops fighting for her right to life
She has no one left to say goodbye.

Her medical assessment comes months later
The score sheet neatly attached.
It drops on the floor of the new tenant
Who sits in her wheelchair
In her lonely one-bedroomed flat

Next corpse arriving

A Tidal Wave by Sally Casey

It was a tidal wave of emotion that took over her. She
shook from head to toe, and nothing she tried helped her
to calm down. Please let this be incorrect she thought,
it's too much for my brain to take in. God, she prayed,
fingers locked, let this be wrong, nothing prepares a

person for this kind of news.

I'm not ready, she thought, no – I don't want it, if I did I would have spoken out, made my voice be heard, I would have expressed my opinion, banged my hand on the table and said firmly, no way is this happening.

I'm exhausted, I'm sleep deprived, I've not eaten a decent meal in days since this was heaped on me. I deserve to be pampered, spoiled, treated very gently until my head knows what my body is aching for.

I'm going to start crying before someone else does, I've got good reason to. This is what nightmares are made of, but I do not want another nightmare coming into my life now. I'm beginning to sweat, and I mean sweat, rivers running down between my swollen breasts, sweaty underarms, sweaty bottom, the list goes on like a bloody waterfall.

Is there any redemption for me from this horror movie that I find myself starring in? I'm going to get on my knees and ask God's forgiveness for all of the bad things I've done in the past. I'm going to make promises that I intend to keep if he will just hear me out and listen to my plea for help.

Dear Lord, I hope that I have caught you at a good time, you are aware of the stress and distress that I am under currently. Please listen to me, and if you are able to grant me this wish I will do my utmost to be the best that I can, I will try to be a better wife, mother, and friend, it is a lot that I am asking of you, but please Lord, make it that my mother in law cannot come to spend three months in my home while she has improvements done to hers and a stair-lift installed.

"Dear Lord, I will never ask anything of you again. AMEN"

He Stood Under a Tree by Sonia James

He stood under a tree unaware he was being watched. Everyone ignores children unless they call attention to themselves and I've learned not to do that. He didn't belong to the village so must just be passing through, painting masterpieces as he went. I could see his easel, so he'd been here a while because he was packing up now. I wanted to laugh out loud. He did look silly in his white smock and big floppy black hat that was so big it looked like it was eating his head. There were no cars in the village today so how did he get here? If I moved now he'd see me so I kept very still as he sauntered over to the river where he piled all his things on the edge of the bank. Just wait until I tell my painting grandad that he might have competition.

He said he was a painter by Anne Finnegan

He said he was a painter, I was enthralled! As I fell into his beautiful dark eyes, strong nose and chiselled jaw line. He leaned languidly against the bar crossing his ankles while supporting himself with one elbow the other in his pocket. I could see under his well-worn fedora a hint of grey that only highlighted his soft white smile. God! I'm in love! He's actually talking to me! The other women around the bar looked on with admiring longing glances. The soft breeze blew his crisp white linen shirt against his chest revealing a tanned strong torso. I gulped my gin and tonic trying to keep my composed cool exterior

From giving away the fanny flutters stirring in the vaults of my lady lands.

"Come and see me at work tomorrow. I would love

to show you my work" Pepe asked in his soft continental accent.

Too bloody right, I though. Hold me back! But staying aloof I nodded with a shy smile "that would be lovely"

Next day buffed, crimped, shaved and primed I set out. Flutters were flittered ready for some action. I felt somewhat confused as I pulled up outside an obviously derelict building looking decidedly lack lustre. I can't see much fluttering happening here!

With that though out came my dream boat looking less dream and more cream.

Holding a roller sodden with magnolia paint "ehhh up love welcome to me and me work. I told you I was a painter dint ah," in the broadest Yorkshire accent.

Just my luck, a painter he said. Serves me right for jumping to conclusions. Although I didn't mind the magnolia ceiling as I lay inspecting it.

Sitting in the Park by Sonia James.

I love to read and always carry a book with me. In the park, most days, weather permitting, when I've been people watching, I'll often read for a while before going home. But just lately I feel I've become invisible! I always try to look smart and tidy, I wear my favourite earrings, my favourite perfume. Is it an age thing, do others cease to notice us as we fade to grey?

My best friend Ted by Sally Casey

Ted, will you say that it was your fault, will you say that you were in the shed, and that the pot of paint fell off the shelf when you stood on Dad's ladders to see if he had hidden my birthday present up high. Will you say that it was your elbow that touched the tin, and that you did not know that it would fall off the shelf onto the floor and splash onto everything and that everything would turn red. My dress looks lovely with lots of lovely red spots on, and you look beautiful with spotty fur. Do you like it TED?

Ted, if you say that you were very naughty, I will share all of my birthday cake with you, and if I get a new bicycle I will let you ride it every day. Will you do that Ted?

But that means Mum will punish Ted for going up on the ladder. And I do love Ted and don't want him to get into trouble. I think that I will ask Miss Lizzie long legs if she will tell Mum that it was her who got up on the ladder in the shed.

Mum loves Miss Lizzie because she was mum's best friend, and I don't think mum will punish her. Come on Ted, let us go and find Miss Lizzie

My Bestest friend by Sonia James

Mummy says I can't take you with me Ted. You know last week when she took me out and you had to stay at home? Well, we went to this place called a Nursery and I have to go there before I'm a bigger girl and go to school. Thing is, you can't come too. No don't cry, I will always love you best and we can play when I get home. Yes I know I am crying too so let's have a really really big hug cos that always makes us feel better. I love you Ted. My bestest friend for ever.

The Brick wall by Hazel Bedford

I'm standing here against this brick wall. Where is everyone? They do not know we are now allowed out.

I feel invisible and wonder if I will morph into this brick wall. Maybe that is what is happened, maybe there are people out there, but they have all become invisible. They too are struggling with lockdown. The days are not getting any easier and just maybe this will be life as we will know it in future. It appears the streets are empty, but they are

Sally Casey: Brick Wall

This scene will not ever change. It will always be brick on brick. I like red brick, it makes me feel safe, it's warm and wraps itself around me like a cosy blanket. Standing here looking at my surroundings I can survey the landscape and send my mind back it times gone by to when this place was fields and farms.

I don't know if people's memories of better days gone by are truth or sentiment. I am cynical of words like better neighbours, we wanted for nothing, kids who were happier so, why then do I sneer at the sky. I was not here then, so what do I know about the past.

As Nan always said, the rich got richer and the poor get poorer. She had nowt and she died the same. Am I bitter, yes, I am bitter, and sad that I couldn't make life easier for her then? My Nan, god's angel on earth to all around her. Her never empty stew pot fed those who needed a dinner! What would health and safety say about that now. No doubt Nan would offer them a bowl.

Well, come on, now, back to the grindstone. What did you promise her? You promised her change, and it won't do that on its own. One hundred red brick family homes you promised her you would build, so these last thirty-eight are not going up on their own. Come on lads, break over, get that hod carrier over here, lots of lovely red bricks to be laid today.

Sitting in the Park by Sally Casey

I love sitting in the park on this bench. My view from here is lovely and with the sun so high in the sky, I am enjoying the heat on my face and shoulders. I'm thankful for the pleasures offered in such pleasant surroundings, and it's so nice to come here early while it's quiet. The tranquillity is balm to my battered soul and spirit.

I need nothing more to lift my spirits, I sit and smile and giggle at the antics of the birds. The bossy ones, the gentle little mothers feeding their babies, the naughty magpies, I enjoy every one of them and rejoice in Mother Nature.

Money cannot buy what I am enjoying for free. I shall continue taking my daily walk and my well-earned rest. I must remember to bring my cushion for my bony bum, and one of these days I'll remember to take my bag with its bottle of water and my unread thriller that I couldn't wait to read, but then again, I would miss the wonder of this, my very own beauty spot made to perfection by my lord above

Teddy Bear by Anne Finnegan

Listen son, you're going to grow out of me it is natural don't let it get you down. I'll always be there for you. I'll always want you to squeeze me tight when you feel alone, use me as a pillow when you restlessly grope for me in the night, throw me high up in the air and smile as I tumble back down into your arms. You can tell me anything, I won't breathe a word and when you cry holding me close, I will soak in those tears and foes that you've been holding for years.

I'll sit on your bed, then up on your drawers, then on top the wardrobe cast away in a box. Finally, to the attic stored away but given life again as your little ones need my ears to cling to swinging here. You'll remember this message from your old teddy bear.

Invisible by Anne Finnegan

I'm sick of being invisible so I put on some clothes.
Do you think they will notice me? Probably not I suppose.
They're so into themselves with their phone's apps n tunes.
If I stood here stark naked which I do every moon.
Think I'll put on a monkey suit and climb all the trees
See if that gets a mention on their daily news feed.

Leaning On The Wall by Sonia James

He's there every day. Leaning, just leaning. Staring into space. I can see him as I look down from my sixth-floor balcony in the flats opposite the back of the precinct. We have lived here for years and the view is nothing to shout about. The back of the precinct! Why does he stand there? The delivery men ignore him, as do the staff from the few remaining shops as they all come and go. Always the same legs lifted against the wall, same dark peaked cap on his head. I can't make out his face from up here but not an old man from the way he stands. So still, never looking right or left, never up nor down. Always ignored, maybe he's not there at all, maybe I've made him up!

Oh, dear Mrs, you've been housebound for too long. I drag myself back into my flat. Open the door

I've left closed for too long. All his clothes piled on his bed. Box of tissues nearby as I pick up one item at a time and fold neatly. Blue quite new Jeans, then his old worn blue sweatshirt with the draw string hood he wore everywhere, still able to pick up the scent of him as I hold it to my face. Then I realized I'm still wearing his black cap, the one with the peak that I used to pull down over his face as he complained, "oh stop it mum!" Dragging out my name like a sigh. My son, oh my son.

Ode to a Fashion-conscious Squirrel by Sonia James

If she is the one that's up there, scratching, scrabbling in my loft. I suppose that she can stay, and No, I haven't gone soft. But now I see she's gorgeous with her red bag and her wrap. I didn't think it was a female, No, I never imagined that.

So now it seems I'm a landlady, I must write down some house rules. But I bet you she'll ignore them, but I tell you I'm no fool. She didn't go to etiquette classes, she hasn't any manners but if I write in red maybe and hang them up on banners? Still, when she is outside with her friends it's peaceful, there is not a sound. And I know she will ignore my rules and keep on scrabbling around.

Paradigm Shift by Tina Cribbin

Hoping for a paradigm shift
As she stepped into a pissed through lift
She didn't resist as she watched her life dreams
Disappear through uneven numbered floors

Middle aged angst
Held in by stretch waist pants

Bought at Stretford market
Her life never seemed to fit inside
The boxes that was planned for her
Her heart was that of an artist

She remembers the could have been
And should have been
Spray painted under the Mancunian Way
Lyrical happening, hoping for a miracle landing
In the concrete interplay

Where she got by
By getting high on teenage dreams
That haunted their ways through
Concrete Balconies and maisonette families

She could still smell beer made promises
That left shaky high heeled footprints
The sounds of arguing, lost keys and tears before
Midnight.

Despite and because of it all
She held her home tight
While she focused on a moon
That wasn't big enough to hold her

So, she flew
And returned to roost
Living life through a different lens
And made amends with her younger self.

Place by Anne Finnegan

I don't know my place, never have. I flit from place to
place morphing into whatever I need to be to fit in! I
change my head and language to suit the place.

A classroom place – correct knowledgeable people in

charge, no messing.

Staff room: Guarded, nosey, coffee, find a seat weird atmosphere academics against creatives.

A boardroom place - armour on, eloquent, informed, interested effective.

A community place: organised, happy, ready for anything, listen, smile, engage, encourage, be there.

A pub space: friends, fun, laughs, woozy stories.

Theatre place: excited, pumping heart, busy head, feel at home in front or behind.

Home space: breathe, enjoy, peace, haven, lock the door.

Head space. Hectic worried muddled tired empty squashed sleep create.

Open space; green, the shore, rain, smell; free ,calm breathe, still.

Zoom: space, square, talk, energy screen blocking emotion (over it!) not the new normal, begging.

So many spaces and not enough me.

Orenda by Sonia James

Orenda: *An invisible magic power believed by the Iroquois to pervade all-natural objects as a spiritual energy.*

Why have we lost it in these so-called modern times? When you watch a plant grow when you want to hug that beautiful tree. When you see a beautiful sunset, do we still feel the hand of God in its glory, or do we hear the school taught scientific explanation? I talk to my plants in the garden and house and thank them for their beautiful display or comfort them when they struggle. Look at the sea and feel its strength, listen to that beautiful bird singing just for you. Remember always to say Thank you, we only pass this way but once.

There is a Place I Like to Sit by Anne Finnegan

There is a place I like to sit.
It's in the shed with all the bits.
When it rains you'll find me there.
Wrapped in a blanket sniffing the air.
The sound and pound of the rain invites me to sleep
And dream of things more lightly.
My boys just nod their heads and giggle
At mum sat in the shed with her cat in the middle.

Building up by Sonia James

Tower blocks were hurriedly built in the 1950s to clear bombed out shops and houses after the second world war. London led the way, but Bristol soon followed and overtook, taking advantage of government subsidies. Rows and rows of terraced houses were soon to be raised to the ground as greed and lack of awareness took over any lingering sensibilities from those who had outgrown their roots, and whole communities were split up and stuck high in the sky, separated, isolated but worse of all some terraces having avoided the builders hammers and dozers, could still be seen from high windows. But there was now separation, local shops and markets had gone too. In the terraces everyone looked out for each other, watched each other's children as they played together in the street. Ten floors up, nowhere to go, nowhere to play, no back door to knock on, no cups of tea made and shared. What does the picture mean to me? The end of community which now, over 60 years later is only being acknowledge with attempts to rectify and monetary grants being thrown hither and thither.

My Mammy says by Anne Finnegan

"My mammy says you have nits. You're crawlin she said, and don't be takin' the Micky out of my hair cut we have a special bowl for this ya know. And I'll point my finger all I want! No I'm not nearly crying so there.

"Bobby tell em"

Bobby stood hand in pockets silently holding me up . "Ah cum on let's go down the canal and catch rats"

I sniffed me snots and nearly tears, and walked away trying to look big as I dragged the heels of me boots behind me coz I had no laces. We walked along the canal. It was dead muddy. We could feel the squelch under our feet, it was seeping into the holes in me boots, my toes rubbed together wet and grimy. Bobby walked ahead coz he was a really good rat spotter. I was still mad at that Nora tellin' me I looked like a kid from the deaf and dumb school across from me house.

Bobby stopped in his tracks. Oh Jaysus, he has one, my eyes darted along and into the canal. Where was it, I couldn't see any black velvet body scurrying for cover or slinking through the water.

Bobby was looking down at his shoes. As I gained on him his eyes were wide watering n wondering "what is it" We both slowly bowed our heads towards Bobby's right foot. There peeping out from under the edge of the toe... a pound note.

Don't You Dare! by Sally Casey

Don't you dare call my Ma stupid. My Da will Knock the head off your Da if I tell him what you said about my Ma. My Ma is the best cook in the world, and we did not get a run around the table for our dinner. We had a big stew with loads of meat in it, and we even had bread and good butter as well with it. We even got jelly and custard after it, So there!

Who's a liar, don't you call me a liar, I'll get my brother to come out and box the ears off of ye, ye cheeky hungry looking tramp. So what did you get for your dinner, probably slop, that's what ye get every day ye skinny rat. Well, come on then, see if I'll run away if ye come after me. I'm not afraid of ye. Remember, I've had a good dinner, more than you, so if you want to start a fight, I'm ready for ye. Go on, get home, see if I care what ye tell your Ma. My Ma would probably give her a slap of the dishcloth if she knocked on our door. Go on, see if I care, I've got more pals than you, just remember, and take your skinny mangy dog with ye. He has probably just bitten me with all the fleas he has. Go on, keep walking, see if I care.

Home is Where the Heart is by Hazel Bedford

My home - I look around and it seems alien to me. A once comfortable, cosy, safe space, is now a place I do not recognise. What has changed? As lockdown has changed to Social Distancing, life seems no better. A roof, 4 walls, several rooms which hold a lot of stories, lots of laughter and tears (not always of sadness), lots of family gatherings and Christmas Dinners. Then why at this moment am I not encouraged to take part in this wealth of feelings. I tell myself all this will pass, and some type of normality will arrive eventually

Home is where the heart is. I hope so, someday soon.

Picture Prompt of Drunk Older Lady

Anne Finnegan: Ohhh I need a sit down "hick", me poor feet are killing me. I feel a bit slurry. Ah feck it I have a fag and a drink at the blob shop I think

Sonia James: Please enlighten this Southerner, what is a blob shop??

Sally Casey: A blob shop was a bar where you could buy a hot red glass of wine for very little money. It would blow the head off you if you weren't aware of its potency. It would bring the dead to life. Extremely popular with men and women. Yates's Wine Lodges were the names I remember. Was only in once. Very warming, you didn't want to leave.

Lil Luckham: I remember going into a blob shop when I was about 17, my Dad didn't speak to me for a week when he found out, according to Bobby only 'certain' ladies went in places like that...

Sonia James: Oh dahlink, yesterday vas de most drrreadful bore, I svear! Dis mornink I must have champagne, lots and lots of champagne or I vill die.

Sally Casey: That bitch, does she think that big breasts and white teeth make her beautiful, what she needs to realise is, we were all like that twenty years ago. Sadly, My Botox went astray. Wot a bastard.

Walking with Dad by Emily Oldfield

As I walked in-step with my Dad, I saw the Waterfoot kitchen with my grandparents' array of owl trinkets, the almost mosaic-like arrangement of fridge magnets. The dusty Manchester streets we walked one dry afternoon, Grandad gesturing to his 'spending money' with a glint in his eye, followed by the warm, soy-heavy fug of a China-town basement buffet; our messy scoops of cold coloured ice cream that made us feel like kings. The rugged, ruin-scattered sides of Cowpe Lowe: his favourite hill where I walked with Hannah – our friendship forged in a battered Industrial Estate flung out from Burnley, those early adulthood years of office work where a chill creeps in. Hannah who drove us down to my grandparent's as soon as the clock struck five, back over the moor, the place on the front room rug where we shared pan-scorched beans and floury potato

The Old House.by Jean Boyode

The old house with its overgrown garden and its silent secret. The children said "look here, I've got something to show you" said Tom.

"I just heard a knock on the door, let's hide" said Sally.

"There's a cat on the grass. Let's follow the cat he is taking us on a journey, it keeps meowing" said Tom

"Let's follow the cat into the house. Look, it's knocked the top off over there, there must be something in there. So, when I went inside the house I saw a mouse, it ran so fast Tom! Tom! The mouse is telling us a secret!"

The Story of Abe by Lil Luckham

Abraham Cullen was born in Manchester in 1903 and died in the city of his birth in 1956, he now lies alone in Southern Cemetery, forgotten because of his weaknesses but now forgiven.

In 1928 Abe met Lily Burney, a lady of ill repute according to some, her crime, she had two bastard children out of wedlock whose father had hot-footed back to Ireland never to be seen again, as Lily's own father had done very soon after her birth.

Lily was a tiny, dark-haired, feisty lady who fell head over heels in love with Abe, little did she know the pain and shame that lay ahead of her when she married him in 1929. She was rejected and shamed by Abe's family who often referred to her as "the whore from Ardwick" and she quickly became aware of what a weak man he was.

Abe and Lily went on to have five children, but neither Abe or his family accepted the 'two bastards', one of them who was deaf and dumb and they simple referred to him as 'the dummy'...

How Lily must have suffered, shamed and treated so badly by the man she adored and his family, yet her deep love for him tied her to him until the end, is it any wonder she started to drink?

During the next few years their relationship became more and more volatile and on many occasions Abe would run home to his mother who would welcome him with open arms with no consideration for Lily left behind with seven children in the hovel she called home.

1956 THE END

In April 1956 Abe left Lily for the final time, by now her

lifestyle was catching up with her, and she was a shadow of the dark-haired girl who had fallen for the weak man. She told her children she would not eat again until her Abe came home, he never did and in May 1956 Lily died of malnutrition... she was 53. Abe was not allowed to attend her funeral and on leaving Philips Park Cemetery his daughter said "if I ever see him again, I will kill him"

In the next few months, his children neither saw nor heard anything of Abe until that fateful knock on the door in October. Abe went to work on Saturday 20th October as a night-watchman at C&A on Oldham Street. Along the way it is believed he enjoyed the company of a local prostitute. Not long after reporting for his shift Abe was murdered during a break in at C&A, it is suspected to steal fur coats. Many people were questioned including his daughter who had uttered those fateful words at her mother's funeral. ABRAHAM CULLEN was my grandfather.

OUR MAN FROM C&A by Lil Luckham

See the man at C&A
He's smart and stylish everyday
But not our Abe, he's weak and wheezy,
Street angel, house devil he's also sleazy.
Lily a woman so tiny, yet passionate and fiery
She adopted his weaknesses as he haunted her dreams.
She could not eat, nor sleep and wasted away,
Felt incomplete, that bastards' indiscretions
Had left her life in smithereens.

Heartbroken and hopeless, self-starved and reckless
Lilly soon passed away.
Down in the stockroom a quick giddy up,

Some fur coats, no knickers he met in a pub
In exchange for a blouse or maybe a skirt
Abe had no idea as the temptress turned away
That the bad guys were waiting on that fateful day.

Weak and unfaithful
A bully and a liar,
Did he really deserve what was to transpire?
A blow to the head for a haul of fur coats
Our man from C&A became Lily's ghost.
But despite his philandering, the pain and the lies,
Despite the fact he made her whole world capsize
Lily would have been happy to be reunited with HER
man from C&A.

To Them by Sally Casey

You came in so quietly so gently with your soft shuffle
shoes and kind words.
You talked of support, partnership, community
development,
Raising aspirations, working together
And a mandate for the future based on trust.

Your words got you through.
You were completely supported.
I fought for the change for the good of the community

I offered you room in my home.
But you wanted the streets, the road, the pubs,
The schools, the parks, the fields, the shops.
Until the very essence of what made my
neighbourhood, my community great

Was slowly dismantled and I began to grieve

A Great Big Dollop of Hope

I went to meet the soft shoed one
Only to find the university was now wearing hob nailed
boots
Which crushed and broke everything in sight in the
need for more.
More rent, more space, more air, more money more
light.

You no longer knew who I was
The one who you made them promises to
The one who supported you.
I could not be heard above the noise of building works
Or be seen between your tall towers
And cranes that light up continually
So even at night there is no rest

Behind your glossy leaflets and benevolent words
Lies the snake that came in and ripped out the heart of
my home my community and told me it was to benefit
us

We finally see the true you
Hiding beneath unheard-of amounts of money
Sitting in offices that are bigger than our homes.

A community now so small we are an island
Squeezed into extinction yet you still you want more

You gave back nothing to us
Now we are not even worth consulting.
Social cleansing already agreed.
Our disposable lives mean nothing to you
But everything to me.

We will not go quietly
We will throw light into the dark corners where you

make your deals
We will come at you with the strongest force – the truth.
Simply the truth.

You are part of our history now
We will ensure our history will not be eradicated
like those buildings and communities past.
You sold us down the river. You sold us down the river
again.

The Kindest Dinner Lady in the World by Sally Casey

A true community activist who educated children's
hearts and minds for decades. Who taught them TO DO
THE RIGHT THING.

My Story by Mazie Reid

I arrived in England from Jamaica on 20th October
1962, it was so cold you couldn't see anything because
everything was really foggy. The worst part was when
I get into the house that was freezing as well! In the
bedroom there was a fireplace with a real fire I could
not believe what was going on. I started crying saying I
want to go back to JA.

To my surprise I was pregnant with my boy was over
the moon, my little girl was born on the 26th December
and we got married on the 26th January it was very
quiet, there were just four of us in this big church on
Mill Lane East. I just wanted to go home but after an
awfully long time I got to know some genuinely nice
people and we were living in Moss Side

After two years we went to live in Birmingham to
stay with my Uncle and family, it was so nice until my

Husband started messing about with other women, it was such a hard road. After a while I just couldn't take the pressure anymore.

I took my children back to Moss Side and then I started looking for somewhere for us to live. I was given a house in Hattersley, it was a nice house in a nice place in the country. I took care of my children on my own until they all grew up.

I moved back to Manchester in 1986 and got a place in Hulme which I immediately liked because the people are nice. I got a job at Withington Hospital, it was so nice to be with people and socialise.

Sometimes we would go to the pub it was nice, but I couldn't drink a lot. I got drunk quite easy, so my drink was two cherry Bs. My life has been rough with illness and everything. But I say life is what you make it. Hulme is a great place to live. I was so glad to find the Aquarius Centre. I started going to groups and everyone is so friendly and helpful.

The Guardian Donkey by John (the quiet man) Sullivan

It was back in Ireland in Cork, so it was. We lived in a small whitewashed house with little windows and a slate roof. I remember fishing for mackerel and lobster down on the bay and selling them at the fish market. I was young then you see but what I always remember was the story told to me by my parents, God rest their souls. You see when I was a baby, I had an older sister called Nancy. Now Nancy's favourite thing in the world was donkeys but we didn't have them. Anyways this one night my mother and father looked out the window they saw a beautiful donkey looking up. It came out of nowhere and they didn't know who owned it. So, the next day they woke up and the donkey had gone. It was also the same day my Sister Nancy died. We think it was the donkey collecting our Nancy's spirit, so she is in heaven, the thing she loved most in the world. It was a comfort to my poor grieving parents, and it was never forgotten.

Lockdown struggles by Mazie Reid

I am talking about my experience of lockdown and how we, the vulnerable people with illness, could not go out and how we were treated. As for myself and the person I care for, it was terrible. The way the over 60's was treated – wow.

When I first received the food parcel it was supposed to be for two people but after two weeks, I stopped them delivering stuff. In my parcel I had tins of spaghetti, tins of tomatoes and beans, a tin of soup, some cereal and rotten bananas. Most of the fruit was out of date, you could not use it. Since lockdown we never get a piece of chicken, fish or fresh meat. But we got lots of chocolate protein bars that were a long time out of date

But what makes it worse is that they deliver your food in see through bags left outside your door. So, it was so degrading. Just because we are ill and old, we don't deserve to be treated like an animal.

Things that make me glad to be alive by Mazie Reid

I give God thanks for another day
I look forward to my writing group
I love phone calls from my family my granddaughter and my little great grandson
I listen to the birds singing

I like making myself useful

I would love to go on a cruise with a couple of my family around the Caribbean and around the Mediterranean I know it would be a joyful adventure. I would also like to see, New York and the Statue of Liberty, Brazil, Cuba, The Virgin Isles and finally, back to Jamaica for the sunshine and remembering my happy school days.

I love my family my grandson, he is so helpful.

My brother who thinks he is my Dad.

And my sisters when we meet up, we always have a great time.

Summers in Bishusha by Esperance Kaligirwa

My grandfather was a Chief. His name was François 'Francky' Gota, and he was a political leader in North Kivu, in the north eastern part of the Democratic Republic of Congo (DRC), which was then called Zaire. I used to go to him for the summer holidays, which lasted for the whole of July and August. Someone would come and pick me up to take me to his farm, just me, the first born, while my younger brother stayed with our parents.

I remember the big barbecue, with all kinds of cooked meats. There were many cattle on the farm, many fields – beans, maize, potatoes, sweet potatoes, tomatoes and cabbages – a big, big farm, growing food to feed all the families that worked the land. A well as cows the farm had chickens, sheep, goats and at least ten horses. When I was young, I was quite plump because I drank so much milk! My grandfather was tall and thin and very fit. He only ate lean meats, with no oil. He had a good, healthy diet full of vegetables. He was a rich man who led groups from many different ethnicities, although he himself was from the Alur, one of the 'Nilotic' peoples who originated in the Nile valley.

My mum, Maureen, was his second child, born in 1934. Her mother died giving birth to her. Later he married again, to a young French woman called Nicole who was the same age as my mum. They met and fell in love on one of his trips to Europe, and she returned with him to the farm, where they had twin daughters. One of my sisters has twins as well, two boys who are now 13 years old. It must run in the family.

I was married at 17. My husband was a doctor – he had studied medicine at the University of Nantes in France – so it was him who took care of me in childbirth. Like me, he was a Catholic. He said we should first marry and then I could finish college. I did go back and graduate, even with my baby bump, and I continued to university, but I became pregnant again and it was too hard with two young children to finish my education. That did make me sad. I had a child every year so I could not continue.

Due to the political situation my husband also became a farmer in later years, and he traded in coffee, tea and other goods. I had a bakery where people came to buy their bread in the morning. I had my office there too. We sold many things.

I have strong memories of those childhood summers on the farm near Bishusha, and of the families who lived there. Their houses were small and round, made from straw, but powered by electricity from a generator. The countryside was beautifully green, and there was a garden full of flowers around my grandfather's house. I remember the big river, and him driving over the bridge in his motor car. I was 26 and had already had my six children by the time he died. He was 104 years old. My mum inherited the farm but when the war came it was all taken away."

CONGOLESE NATIONAL ANTHEM

This was the national anthem when I was at school, during the time when Mbuto was president and the DRC was still Zaire:

Zaïrois dans la paix retrouvée,	Zairians in regained peace,
Peuple uni, nous sommes Zaïrois	United people, we are Zairians
En avant fier et plein de dignité	Forth we go, proud and full of dignity
Peuple grand, peuple libre à jamais	Great people, forever free
Tricolore, enflamme nous du feu sacré	Tricolor – ignite us with sacred fire
Pour bâtir notre pays toujours plus beau	To build our ever more beautiful country
Autour d'un fleuve Majesté (2×)	Around a majestrial river
Tricolore au vent, ravive l'idéal qui nous relie aux aïeux, à nos enfants	Tricolor in the wind, revive the ideal which connects us to our ancestors, to our children:
Paix, justice et travail.	Peace, justice and work.

Now the anthem has reverted to an earlier version. We sing it in French, the official language, but I also speak Lingala, Swahili and six tribal languages.

Debout Congolais, Unis par le sort, Unis dans l'effort pour l'indépendance,	Arise Congolese people, united by fate, united in the struggle for independence
Dressons nos fronts, longtemps courbés	Let us raise up our long-bended heads
Et pour de bon prenons le plus bel élan, dans la paix, O peuple ardent, par le labeur, nous bâtirons un pays plus beau qu'avant, dans la paix.	And let us for ever follow the loveliest desire, in peace, oh ardent people, and through our toil build a country more beautiful than before, in peace.
Citoyens, entonnez, l'hymne sacré de votre solidarité, Fièrement, saluez, l'emblème d'or de votre souveraineté, Congo.	Citizens, sing your sacred hymn of solidarity, Proudly greet the golden symbol of your sovereignty, Congo.
Don béni (Congo) des aïeux (Congo), O pays (Congo) bien aimé (Congo), Nous peuplerons ton sol et nous assurerons ta grandeur.	Blessed gift (Congo) of our ancestors , Oh beloved country (Congo), We will populate your soil and ensure your greatness.
O doux soleil (trente juin) du trente juin, (Jour sacré) Sois le témoin (jour sacré) de l'immortel, serment de liberté	Oh sweet sun, on 30th June, the Holy day, Be the witness of the immortal oath of freedom
Que nous léguons, à notre postérité, pour toujours.	That we bequeath to our descendants, forever.

The Dream by Hazel Bedford

This is a dream that I had last night. It started with a lot of our Aquarius friends. Away on holiday. The only way I can describe the place is it was like Eastern Europe meets the Middle East. It was the day we were due to fly home; we were having afternoon tea all sat at trestle type tables, it came to the time for Tea and Cake. I chose a cupcake with a gold heart on, put it on my plate and went to get cups of tea for everyone. Not happy when I returned to my seat, someone was eating my cake, and of course, I blamed everyone else for not looking after my cake.

Before we had to leave for the airport Sonia decided she wanted to go and look at a particular artefact... so I decided to go along with her, Big Mistake.

We boarded a train, well it looked like a train from the outside, but once inside you went along a corridor (which had a Russian Soldier on guard) went down a flight of steps into a room with brick walls – no windows.

When we arrived at our destination (this was the 1st time Sonia told me off for dawdling crossing a road), cannot remember what it was we were looking for. Anyway, now it's time to join the group for our journey home. Sonia decided she would purchase a scarf like the women were wearing (we are now in the Middle Eastern section). However, the item purchased look more like a Bonnet to wear with a Crinoline Dress than a scarf (sorry Sonia if you will invade my dreams).

Once again in trouble for not keeping up with said woman, dawdling again. Once back on the train with no windows we hoped we had left at the right place. We walked around but nothing seemed familiar. THEN I WOKE UP.

If there is a moral to this dream... Once we are all back together stay clear of me if there is CAKE.

Response to Dream by Sally Casey

That was a lovely narration of your dream H, I was with you the whole way, but that cross woman called Sonia, she probably ate your cake, brought you to strange places on a journey to nowhere and got you lost.

The moral of the story is:
1. Do not go off with a woman whose intent on buying you a burka
2. Do not travel with said woman unless you have your bus/train ticket on you
3. Do not invite her on your travels, was she trying to sell you in exchange for said head gear?

Johnny Skidmarks by Sally Casey

The kids laugh at me in the school playground, they make up rhymes about me, and the girls skip to them rhymes. Me mates call me skidders, but they are not my mates, mates do not treat you like that if they are your mates.

I have asked me Mam, why did you marry someone called Skidmarks? She said, I didn't marry anyone, that was my name growing up. I said, why did you not marry me Dad, she said, he ran away and left me on my own to tell my Mam that I was having a baby. Me Mam threw me out, and that's why we live in our little house like it is. I don't have any money to buy us nice things, but I do love you Johnny, and I am sorry that you don't have a Dad, and I am sorry that you don't like your name.

Are you dead unhappy Johnny, she asked? Yea I am a bit I said. The kids call me names, and I don't know who my gran and my grandad and cousins are. That makes me unhappy, and I don't like seeing you sad Mam.

I am alright Johnny, she said, we get by, and you are getting big now, you know maybe Mister Bloom might have a job for you as a messenger boy soon.

I set to thinking, and went to see Mister Bloom, and he did have a job for me. Straight after school and all day Saturday. I was alright with that, and I could help Mam.

Cycling on me messenger bike with the basket full gave me so called mates a great laugh, they would shout after me, watch out for the Skidmarks on your saddle Johnny. I decided enough was enough, this had to stop, how would I ever get a girlfriend if all she ever heard was my surname being shouted after me.

I am going to pay them all back for the way they have hurt me all my life.

Cycling all over town is a great way to see how people live. Who has more than others, who gives you a tip after wheeling their order up the big hill, who complains to Mister Bloom if there is bread is squashed, who leaves their doors open, who leaves bicycles outside overnight.

Within a couple of months, I had a nice little nest egg stashed away for me and Mam.

I would bring her home little treats on Saturday night. A nice slice of ham slipped out of some customers order, a couple of tomatoes that Mister Bloom gave me as well as a couple of peaches and over ripe bananas that needed to be eaten soon. A squashed loaf that Mam did not mind having. She was glowing with happiness, and she was starting to look better also.

What was the harm in rifling through a bag of clothes that a lady asked me to take to the charity shop that I would be passing by on my bicycle. Mam was so much warmer in her cardigans and decent shoes that I told her people gave to me.

I found nothing wrong in going round the back of the houses where I knew some of my tormentors lived and relieved them of footballs, boots, jerseys and shorts off the line.

I went back some nights when all was quiet and helped myself to bicycles, scooters, things that had been left out because they did not care about them.

I had found a man who had a second hand shop, and it was him who first put the idea in my head when he asked me while I was delivering his groceries if I ever came across any good items while out on the bike. I now had someone who asked no questions of anything that I brought him, and he paid okay, so it suited the both of us.

I am getting a bit big now for delivering to people's houses. Mister Bloom said he would like me to come into the shop and work with him full time. I'll be sad to stop. But I'll be ok. I have saved up all the money that I have earned. No one was any the wiser that I was involved in anything that ever went missing, after all who would blame little skidders, he was useless.

When I am eighteen me and Mam are moving to a better house. We have nice beds now; Mam has her fireside chair with the plump cushion on that she loves. We have enough coal stocked in the cellar to do us for a few years. Whoever misses a shovel of coal from their delivery on a Monday, and my basket had a secret hiding place at the bottom, away from any prying eyes.

I have been reading up in the library, and I now know that I will use some of my money to do what I have always wanted to do. I am going to rid myself and Mam of that awful name that has plagued us all our lives. Soon, no one will ever call us SKIDMARKS again

The Noisy Garden by Sonia James

Two hours on Sunday I worked in our shared garden
Bending down made me fart, oh I do beg your pardon
But my grumpy neighbour Flo, just tutted and walked away.
She'll forgive me later; her selfish son is due today.
She rarely ventures out, only to buy him tasty treats
He'll eat all that she provides, fancy chocolates, piles of meat
He comes to bring his washing, and boy can he slam doors!
He'll eat her food, then sit in her chair, I can hear his snores
I want to scream and shout in her ear,
But she won't listen to what I say.
He's her darling, her dear.

Christmas Cheer by Sally Casey

We all knew that Christmas dinner would be the best. It always was. There would be loads of everything to eat. There would be no problem in asking for seconds of everything. Turkey, ham, roast potatoes, cabbage, anything you wanted, except, you had to be careful of asking could you have some lemonade or orange juice.

You see, these treats came by way of my father being a long distance driver, and over the winter months he would drive all over the country making sure that pubs and shops were well stocked with all kinds of goodies that people could only afford to buy for the festive season.

He carried hams, boxes of delicious biscuits, sacks of apples, oranges, etc. But best of all were the crates of Taylor Keith lemonade, and orange juice. These were the best of fizzy drinks, bought for you if you happened to be the chosen one to go out with your parents, and they inevitably would end up in a pub for a drink. You would be given a glass of your choice, and you relished it, and then bragged to all who would listen to you at home about it.

My father might be away for a couple of nights, and we would wait in anticipation to see if he would bring home any crates with him. He may bring in a crate of large bottles or a couple of small crates depending on who he had short-changed on their order that he had delivered that day. That would continue for a couple of weeks and depending on what he was delivering to whom or where, he always came home with booty. He never uttered a word, but we knew that he hadn't bought these goodies for us, he was too mean to spend money on us, but did we care, not one bit.

He would open a large bottle and share it out with the seven of us children. It was nectar to us, better than any champagne you ever tasted, you did not leave a drop in your glass. That would be the end of our tasting session until Christmas.

He would open up the sideboard, and put all of the bottles that he had acquired on his works journeys into it, lock the sideboard, and say, you can have what you want at Christmas. It was like putting cream cakes on the table and telling seven children not to touch them.

Well, my older brothers were master burglars when it came to opening a sideboard, they would pull it out from the wall, get a screwdriver, remove the back panel, and Hey Presto, they pulled out a large bottle of white lemonade. It had to be white lemonade, not orange juice. You see, the bottle had to be refilled with water, the top resealed and put back into the sideboard. No evidence was left for my father's all seeing eyes. We weren't too greedy, after all you had to think ahead to Christmas. We were promised a slow death by our brothers if we ever revealed this secret. We all knew the punishment that would befall all of us if Da found out what we had been doing.

Christmas dinner, we are all around the table and Da does his proud father bit. He hands the sideboard key to one of the boys and says, bring a small bottle for the little ones, and you bigger ones can have a large bottle each. The little ones had to have a bottle of orange juice just in case, But when the large bottles started to appear, we would look at each other knowing that maybe all of us were bound to get a bottle of stale water that had been in there for weeks on end. You had to take what was given to you, no matter what the colour of the contents. You knew who had lost by the looks on their faces. We would sit there holding in the laughter, knowing if it got out of hand that we would be removed from the table, and that was the end of your Christmas dinner.

To this day I remember my big brothers, how our Christmas started so early for us, and how a few bottles of illicit lemonade could cause such fun for us along with the fear of being caught out. My father was a hard man who did not have a lot of time for his seven children, he would deny us the basic tools for school. We were without good shoes for the winter. But yet he would do nice things for us when it suited him. I believe that he was a man of his day, brought up by a mother who treated her sons like princes, but her son, my father, turned into a frog.

I loved Christmas dinner with my children when they were small, and I could not have cared less how many bottles or cans of juice that they drank that day. They all know the story of Christmas Day in my home, and the antics that we got up to. We were luckier than lots of other families, but who sees that when you are a child who expected a scooter for Christmas, and got a used embroidery set that had belonged to her cousin.

Moaners by Sonia James

Are we now just a country of moaners?
Because being afraid is no excuse
I think I'm on the side of the loners
Although I'm definitely no recluse
Yes, it's hard to let go and let others decide,
We are all used to freedom unbounded
We cannot go out, but we don't have to hide.
But it can depress even the strongest to hear,
How downbeat the deciders sounded

Sonia James: Hi Irish. Lovely day, blackbird still not copped off he's singing his heart out on the apex of a roof, or maybe he's singing self-congratulatory trills!

Sally Casey: How thrilling for your blackbird, wish I'd copped off, I'd be singing my tonsils dry. Some birds have all the luck

Three Generations by Sally Casey

I am the littlest one at the back, my Da is wearing the grey suit, my Granda is the other one. He has come to stay with us for a few weeks because granny is in hospital. Granny is lovely, She is very squishy when she gives a hug. She smells like nice soap, and she always has sweets in her apron pocket. Granda is nice as well, but he smells of that stuff that he sniffs up his nose. I think it is called snuff. I don't like the feel of Granda's jacket either, it's very rough, and I do be raging when he ruffles my hair like I am a baby.

I am a big boy now, Ma said I could go on the walk with Da and Granda, but I was not to talk, because they had a lot to tell each other. And if I got in the way I wouldn't be let go with them until I learnt some manners.

Well here I am just following them. I think that I am being a good boy. Just look at the way I can keep up with them as they walk down to the park. I am big enough now to fold my arms around my back just like them. I could not do that if I wasn't a big boy, could I? I'm nearly two and a half now, and soon Ill be three. When I am four I will be able to go to school with my big brother who is nearly six.

Mam said that I have more sense than him, he is always getting into trouble. He gets lots of smacks from Mam, and he is always sent to bed without cocoa and toast. I always get my cocoa; I really like it at bed time. It is so nice. My brother says that I get to go out with Da too many times. He will pinch me on the arms tonight when we go to bed as punishment because he was not allowed to come with us.

Aw well, I'm going to try and keep up with them, although my legs and my arms are getting heavy. It's really hard being a big boy. I'm going to ask Da to put me up on his shoulders for a while.

It's hard being a big boy. I think Ill ask Da to carry me on his shoulders. I don't think he will call me a sissy. Do You?

Writers Beware by Sally Casey

Writers beware, Downing Street are looking for a speech writer for blethering Boris. It seems that whoever wrote his piece yesterday forgot to ask him if he understood the wording on the pages. He muttered something incoherent and went out of the room. The rest is history.

It was like he was delivering a few lines from the hokey pokey. Yes, You can go out but you must be alert. Boris has become A Lert.

Definition of a Lert: One who does not know his arse from his elbow

Sally Casey: No, boredom is off the list (YET). Well I think the rash on my forehead is now not teenage acne as I was hoping, so Sherlock Holmes has been invited to check me over. I'm hoping Pierce Brosnan may appear, but just another fantasy.

What are you doing up reading at dawn Sonia? If you were busy you would still be asleep. I'm glad you don't start eating at that hour, you would never get through a doorway. I think we had rain last night, it gives me a day off from watering.

The Holiday by Hazel Bedford

Hello everyone has anyone just heard that plane go over. I HOPE it's not that naughty man MR CUMMINGS going on holiday. If it is I will be throwing my toys out of the pram. We have missed our holiday this year and I begrudge anyone who can go on holiday. Oh, dear what am I turning into, a horrible grumpy old woman.

Boris the Dope by Sally Casey

Us oldies can meet up with one person from tomorrow, keeping our distance. Wow. Everyone else can meet up with five more persons and keep to the two-metre distance. That is what had been said on radio 4 and hi everyone, another day in prison

Boo Boris the Dope

Boo Dominic the liar

Sonia James: Oh Irish, you have not turned onto a horrible grumpy old woman. You've always been like that! Oh sorry Irish, it was H that said that. Too late to change it now.

Sally Casey: Naughty Sonia, Me grumpy, never been heard of. Sweet as a lily am I Xxx Morning all, another day in paradise, but we can meet up with someone else from today. Yea yea.

Hope you are all well.

It's Only Legal by Tina Cribbin

Morning all. Yes Sally! Any plans now that you are all legal. Just to remind you, you can only have sex if the person lives with you. I wonder how quickly people move in together and then move out

I Can Advertise by Sally Casey

I can advertise. Mature lady invites handsome person for some afternoon delight and see what or who materialises from it. I'm actually becoming reclusive and it's not a bother, my days are morphing into each other. That's how they lived up to the nineties when the world opened up. I need to get a life back again.

Losing and Winning by Sonia James

I was having a terrible fight with the gambling devil on my back.

And then I wanted to shoot my boss, he gave me the sack!

He found me in the stationary cupboard with Christopher from accounts

We were playing Strip Poker, I was losing HUGE amounts

I was really, really embarrassed sitting there in just my knickers

And he'd thrown the door wide open, I could hear the office sniggers

But now looking back, it's a good thing that I lost my job

Because I'm having abandoned sex with a security man named Bob

Rock on Tommy! By Sally Casey

You dirty bitch, that Christopher told me that he had the hots for me, and now you are saying that you played strip poker with him in a cupboard. I hope it is not the cupboard where I leave my shopping bag when I slip out to Tesco in my lunch break to get something for my tea.

You are a tramp, and do not blame it on the boss for sacking you. I hope Bob gets rid of you also, you Tart. He is too good for you. Now see how you will manage on dole money. I would love to be there and have a good snigger when you go to the food bank. This is

Karma, payback for all the nasty things you've said to me at work and all the trouble you caused. Well Suck it up, and Rock on Tommy.

Mr Nutkin by Sonia James

Guinness have photographed the damage Mr Nutkin has done in my loft. He's chewed through all the extractor pipes, and that's how he gets in from the roof, down the pipe! They 'might' put cage on roof over the pipe outlet. He took photos and will show his boss. I said leave the pipes as they are and just put cage on roof. Big sucking in of air as he said, pipes have to be repaired they expel your damp air and steam. I told him I don't use them, more sucking in of air and an attempted lecture but I distracted him by admiring his big torch. He showed me all of its impressive features and left a very happy workman.

The Torch by Sally Casey

You old tart, I knew you were up for it with anyone who had his torch in his hand. And then to show you how its features work, well you should have closed your eyes and prayed that he either would or wouldn't ask you if you would like to hold it. Tart.

And as for your rodent, I'm sure you've been inviting him in for treats. Shameful Hussy. If the man with the torch tells his mates, you will be inundated with requests to view their truncheons, chisels, plungers etc. The list is endless.

You will be requesting a rent reduction for entertaining Guinness Staff. Your name will be spread all over the wash house, Mrs. James

Get back in your box by Sonia James

Well it takes one to know one Irish. Get back in your box!

I Never Took My Slip Off by Anne Finnegan

My mum had a friend. A little woman who wore a head scarf tied deliberately under her chin. Now and again you could see some curlers. Always a skirt (straight) and a cardigan, American tan tights, click heels or slippers. 4.5-foot-tall with a kind face, a pronounced Dublin accent and lots of children. She one said during a whispered frank discussion around sex "well I don't know how I got 9 children I never took me slip off" folding her arms under her bust looking flummoxed.

Another older lady around 86 years old talking to me about her days as a land girl and in the R.A.F I asked "what did you do in the R.A.F"

She answered, "3 years!"

What Writing to Me Means by Sally Casey

Writing to me means that I can be me, or I can become someone who I wish to be, a person that I would never want to know, or I can make up a story that will either make me happy that I have written it, or once written, I can delete if I want to. Writing can take me back into the recesses of my mind. It can conjure up memories of past times, happy, and not so happy ones.

Happy memories flow for me when I am writing. I find it a very pleasant experience to sit and write of things I have done or seen, places that I have visited, wistfully look back on chances that I have missed, and I can bash away at the keys when I am writing about my family and friends old and new.

Unhappy memories stick to my fingers like jam, and I am not allowed to write. I do not find a good reason to tap any keys when a subject, or a thought, or a dark memory from the past wishes to push itself forward, looking for space on the page to be included in my story, I go into a place of safety where I know its alright to be there and be me, the child, again. That is something that I want to work on in my own head to overcome, stick my two fingers up at, and say to myself, there you are Girl, go for it. Write down what you like and do it for you.

I must be comfortable in my head when I am writing. When I sit down to write, whether it's a small piece or other, I know how I want to feel when the piece is finished. I am either going to be happy, as that is my reason for starting it, and if I read the piece out to my group, I am always pleased if they tell me that it is funny, witty and good, and that they have enjoyed it. I do not have confidence in my writing, or in my ability to deliver good pieces, but I find joy in sitting here writing what I know to be my thoughts, my ideas, and my memories of yesterday, and today.

Reading has always been a huge passion of mine since I was a small child. I think that I was in awe of the writers, who were they, where they lived, where their talent came from, and how they got the opportunity to create these books that held me enthralled. I held them up on a pedestal then, and I still do that to this day.

The late Maeve Binchy was my favourite writer of all time. I soaked up every word of every novel that she wrote, and I so wished to be somewhere near her to ask her how it all happened, how did she think up her characters, what was it that gave her the calmness and the ability to write all of those best sellers. I would have so loved to know her. It was with sadness that I learned that she was no less a mortal being like everyone else, and that she had her issues in her life also. It did not affect my appreciation of her amazing talent, it just reminded me that behind every closed door lies another story.

I will carry on with my writing, with the hope that I will learn from every line that I write, that I will listen intently to other people when they share their poems, stories and ditties, that I will stop criticising my writing, and remember too that I am only a mortal being. I so enjoy being in my writing group. I get the confidence to write more for each session, and by my contribution to the group, I feel that I can encourage the other members to also continue with their writing.

The Flashing Knees by Sonia James

Being so useless on Facebook, I've seen quite by chance that Irish has another award! Flipping heck Mrs, you'll have to build a new shelf to put them all on. Bit greedy though don't you think? And you, in that flashy red dress! Were you flashing your knees?

The Flashy Red Dress by Sally Casey

That flashy red dress has had a few outings I tell you. I haven't won anything I am on the short list, and you know where short lists end up, yes, you are right. You are being very stinky about me today, who or what rattled your cage, if it was a big Doberman dog, I hope he ran away when he saw the bad mood that you were in. Be a nicer old person tomorrow, you will be pleased with

yourself

<u>Sonia James</u>: Look. If you don't want to be remarked upon you shouldn't flash your knees on Facebook. So there! Don't know why I love you

<u>Sally Casey</u>: And I don't know why I don't report you for being so bad to me. Just as well I love you

<u>Sally Casey</u>: Hazel and I planted carrots, cabbage salad and beetroot on Wednesday, I thought I'd end up in A&E but I survived. I too am so bored I could kick you if I were near enough, this rain is torturing me. I have the heating on and a rug over my knees. Effin' getting older, does it get much better?

<u>Sonia James</u>: No Irish it's all downhill from here. RIGHT, enough of this moaning. We've got writing to do!